KANTAR
FOR THE DEFENSE
VOLUME 1

Published by
Melvin Powers
WILSHIRE BOOK COMPANY
12015 Sherman Road
No. Hollywood, California 91605
Telephone: (213) 875-1711 / (818) 983-1105

Printed by

HAL LEIGHTON PRINTING COMPANY
P.O. Box 3952
North Hollywood, California 91605
Telephone: (213) 983-1105

Library of Congress Catalog Card Number: 82-063189
ISBN 0-87980-400-9
Printed in the United States of America

CONTENTS
PAGE

FOREWORD

"Kantar for the Defense" is a compendium of 100 practical defensive problems. The level ranges from intermediate to semi-advanced. There are no "braincrushers". On the other hand, there are very few "patsies".

With few exceptions all of the hands can be defeated with logical defense. Although you may think that you have just been given a big hint, in reality you haven't. Good defenders think that every hand can be beaten and all plays are directed toward this goal.

True, in tournament bridge you have to worry about the dreaded overtrick(s), in this quiz you don't. JUST TRY TO BEAT THE HAND.

You are to assume that you are playing with an expert partner. He can definitely be trusted — but no defender is an island. He will also trust your leads and signals.

You have decided to lead fourth best vs. both suit and notrump, and the king from ace-king vs. suit contracts. Furthermore, the lead of a jack denies a higher honor and the lead of a nine or ten shows either top of a sequence or two higher honors, including the one directly above the card that is led. (9 shows Q 10 9, K 10 9, or A 10 9, 10 shows K J 10 or A J 10). You are also leading the Q from A K Q vs. suit contracts. Partner is expected to give count, not attitude, if he reads the lead. He will.

You have also decided to play standard count and attitude signals although your partner wanted to play upside down signals.

The opponents aren't doing anything very fancy either. They are playing a 15 – 17 point one notrump range, 20 to a bad 22 two no-trump range, weak jump overcalls, weak two bids, and will seldom open with a four card major unless it is a strong suit. An asterisk will be used to describe any unusual bid they make.

In order to do well on these hands, you are going to have to both count and visualize. Your thought process should start with the bidding trying to work out declarer's most likely distribution and point count. Next, you will have to work out the meaning of partner's opening lead as well as placing the key missing honors around the table. Furthermore, if you are not in the habit of counting declarer's tricks as the play develops, you will be after you read this book.

Finally, you must be prepared to put certain cards in partner's hand if you absolutely need those cards to defeat the contract.

If two lines of defense present themselves (they will) select the one that needs the least from partner's hand.

This will be a difficult quiz to score because there are many problems which have as many five or more questions attached to them.

It is most important that you tackle each of these questions separately, without looking at the next question before you answer. Many times the answer to the previous question will be in the next question. (In which case it may not appear in the solution.)

Most other quiz books bring you up to the "big" play by telling you what to do before the big play comes up. Not this one. You have to get to the "big play" by yourself.

A few more tips. The titles are not meant to contain helpful hints. Don't knock yourself out trying to read something into them.

You are up against a competent declarer who can be counted on to play both logically and deceptively, so be on your toes.

At the end of the book each problem is classified according to theme. You should make note of which problems you happen to have any "accidents" with (don't defeat). If you find that your errors are falling into any specific categories, so much the easier to work them out.

Above all, the idea of the book is to teach you to "think defense" while somehow still having fun! Fun means that you will look forward to defending after you have read this book. If you don't, I've blown it.

Eddie Kantar
Los Angeles, California

(1)　THREE ACES

East-West vulnerable
Dealer South

North
♠ 7 6
♡ K 5
◇ K Q J 9
♣ A Q 6 3 2

West (you)
♠ A 8
♡ A J
◇ A 8 7 6 4 3
♣ 10 9 8

South	West	North	East
Pass	1 ◇	Pass	Pass
1 ♠	Pass	2 NT	Pass
3 ♠	All Pass		

Opening lead: ◇ A

1. Partner plays the ◇ 2, declarer the ◇ 5. Who has the missing diamond?
2. What do you play at trick two, and why?

THREE ACES (Solution)

North
♠ 7 6
♡ K 5
◇ K Q J 9
♣ A Q 6 3 2

West
♠ A 8
♡ A J
◇ A 8 7 6 4 3
♣ 10 9 8

East
♠ 9 5 2
♡ 8 7 6 4 3
◇ 2
♣ K 7 5 4

South
♠ K Q J 10 4 3
♡ Q 10 9 2
◇ 10 5
♣ J

1. Declarer. With 10-2 doubleton partner would have started an echo.
2. The ♡ A. This is to be followed with the ♡ J. Upon winning the ♠ A you give your partner a ◇ ruff and then ruff a ♡ in return with your lovely ♠ 8 which just tops dummy's ♠ 7. Why am I so good to you?

KEY LESSON POINTERS

1. WHEN PARTNER LEADS AN ACE AND DUMMY COMES DOWN LOADED IN THE SUIT, THIRD HAND GIVES COUNT IF HE HAS NOT SUPPORTED THE SUIT, SUIT PREFERENCE IF HE HAS.
2. WHEN HOLDING THE TRUMP ACE YOU ENJOY THE LUXURY OF NOT RUSHING TO GIVE PARTNER AN IMMEDIATE RUFF. SOMETIMES IT IS BETTER TO VOID YOURSELF FIRST—THEN WHEN YOU GIVE PARTNER A RUFF, HE CAN RETURN THE FAVOR.

(2)   NO SIREE!

North-South vulnerable
Dealer West

North
♠ K 9 8 7
♡ J 10 9 4
♢ 3
♣ A 7 6 5

East (you)
♠ 6 3
♡ A K 8 7 6 5
♢ A 10 4 2
♣ 2

West	North	East	South
Pass	Pass	1 ♡	1 ♠
3 ♣*	4 ♠	All Pass	

* Preemptive in competition
Opening lead: ♡ 2

You win the ♡ K as declarer drops the Q.
1. What do you return at trick two?
2. You return the ♡ 8 which partner ruffs. Partner returns the
   ♢ 6 to your ace. What do you return at trick four?

NO SIREE!   (Solution)

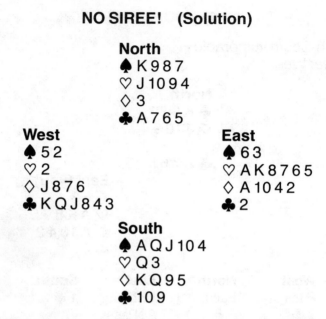

North
♠ K 9 8 7
♡ J 10 9 4
◇ 3
♣ A 7 6 5

West
♠ 5 2
♡ 2
◇ J 8 7 6
♣ K Q J 8 4 3

East
♠ 6 3
♡ A K 8 7 6 5
◇ A 10 4 2
♣ 2

South
♠ A Q J 10 4
♡ Q 3
◇ K Q 9 5
♣ 10 9

♡ 8. In order to make the right defensive plays on this hand you must remember that partner did *not* open 3 ♣ which he probably would have done with a seven card suit. Partner probably has six clubs and your job is to protect his probable club winner to go along with your three red suit winners.

What you have to do is kill the heart discards before declarer can draw trumps. Start by giving partner a heart ruff at the same time telling him which suit you want returned.

When partner obliges with a diamond, return, a second *low* heart forces declarer to ruff. Having killed both heart discards, declarer must lose a club at the end.

KEY LESSON POINTERS

1. IT IS VITAL FOR THE DEFENDERS TO KILL DISCARDS BEFORE DECLARER CAN DRAW TRUMPS.
2. SOMETIMES THE BEST WAY TO KILL DISCARDS IS TO GIVE PARTNER A RUFF WHILE STILL RETAINING CONTROL OF THE SUIT.
3. WHEN GIVING PARTNER A RUFF, DO NOT GET CARELESS. THE SIZE OF THE CARD YOU PLAY TELLS PARTNER WHICH SUIT YOU WANT RETURNED.
4. SOME PARTNERSHIPS PLAY WEAK JUMP SHIFT RESPONSES IN COMPETITION. THESE RESPONSES GENERALLY SHOW SIX CARD SUITS WITH A LIMITED POINT COUNT.

(3) COMPETITIVE AUCTION

North-South vulnerable
Dealer North

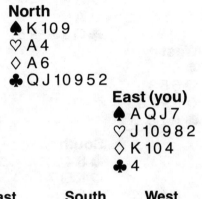

North
♠ K 10 9
♡ A 4
♢ A 6
♣ Q J 10 9 5 2

East (you)
♠ A Q J 7
♡ J 10 9 8 2
♢ K 10 4
♣ 4

North	East	South	West
1 ♣	Dbl.	Rdbl.	1 ♢
Pass	Pass	1 NT	Pass
3 NT	All Pass		

Opening lead: ♢ 3

1. Dummy plays low, which diamond do you play?
2. You win the ♢ K, declarer playing the ♢ 5, what do you play to trick two?

COMPETITIVE AUCTION   (Solution)

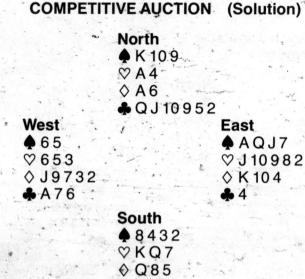

North
♠ K 10 9
♡ A 4
◇ A 6
♣ Q J 10 9 5 2

West
♠ 6 5
♡ 6 5 3
◇ J 9 7 3 2
♣ A 7 6

East
♠ A Q J 7
♡ J 10 9 8 2
◇ K 10 4
♣ 4

South
♠ 8 4 3 2
♡ K Q 7
◇ Q 8 5
♣ K 8 3

The ♠ 7. Partner needs a club trick to defeat this contract. If partner has a club trick all you need to do is shift to your low spade. Partner wins his club trick and returns a ♠. You must get three spades along with the ◇ K and partner's presumed club trick.

KEY LESSON POINTERS

1. DON'T OVERLOOK SIMPLE DEFENSES. THEY ARE USUALLY THE BEST.
2. CONSIDER THIS LAYOUT AT NOTRUMP.

> **North**
> ♠ K 5
>
> **West**   **East (you)**
> ♠ 4 2   ♠ A Q J 8 3
>
> **South**
> ♠ 10 9 7 6

ASSUME THAT YOU MUST ATTACK SPADES FROM YOUR SIDE. IT IS CLEARLY RIGHT TO LEAD A LOW SPADE RATHER THAN AN HONOR OR ACE AND ANOTHER. BY LEADING LOW YOU RETAIN COMMUNICATIONS WITH PARTNER AND INSURE FOUR TRICKS NO MATTER WHICH ONE OF YOU REGAINS THE LEAD.

IN THE DIAGRAM SITUATION YOU KNEW PARTNER WOULD BE THE ONLY ONE THAT COULD POSSIBLY GET THE LEAD. IF YOU WERE THE ONE WITH THE OUTSIDE ENTRY YOU WOULD HAVE TO ATTACK SPADES BY LEADING AN HONOR AND HOPING THE REMAINING SPADES WERE DIVIDED 3-3.

(4)   WHAT'S GOING ON?

East-West vulnerable
Dealer South

                    North
                    ♠ 10 8 6 2
                    ♡ 7 6 5
                    ◇ A K J 4
                    ♣ Q J

West (you)
♠ Q J 9 5
♡ 8 3
◇ 8 5
♣ A 6 5 4 3

South	West	North	East
1 ♡	Pass	2 ◇	Pass
2 ♡	Pass	3 ♡	All Pass

Opening lead: ♠ Q

Partner wins the trick with the ♠ A and returns the ♠ 3 to declarer's ♠ K.

1. Who has the remaining spade?
   Declarer plays off the ♡ A K, partner following with the ♡ J and then the ♡ 9.
2. What does partner's play signify?
3. At trick five declarer leads the remaining spade towards dummy, which spade do you play?
4. You win with the ♠ J and partner discards the ♣ 10. Now what do you play?

WHAT'S GOING ON?   (Solution)

North
♠ 10 8 6 2
♡ 7 6 5
◊ A K J 4
♣ Q J

West
♠ Q J 9 5
♡ 8 3
◊ 8 5
♣ A 6 5 4 3

East
♠ A 3
♡ J 10 9
◊ Q 10 9 6 3
♣ K 10 7

South
♠ K 7 4
♡ A K Q 4 2
◊ 7 2
♣ 9 8 2

1. Declarer. Had partner two remaining spades he would have returned the higher.
2. J 10 9. His play shows you where his sequence starts and where it ends. With Q 10 9 he plays the ten and then the nine, with 10 9 8, the ten and then the eight.
3. The ♠ J. You do not want partner to waste his trump, do you?
4. A low club to partner's ♣ K (declarer has already turned up with 12 high card points so he cannot have the ♣ K and pass 3 ♡). Furthermore, declarer must have two diamonds and three clubs rather than vice versa, or else he would have drawn the last trump before leading a spade. Partner returns a club and your final club play allows partner to make his ♡ 10.

KEY LESSON POINTERS

1. WHEN RETURNING PARTNER'S SUIT RETURN THE HIGHER OF TWO REMAINING CARDS.
2. WHEN FOLLOWING SUIT IN TRUMPS WITH A SEQUENCE, START AT THE TOP AND PLAY THE BOTTOM ONE NEXT.
3. WHEN PARTNER DISCARDS A HIGH SPOT CARD HE CAN BE SHOWING COUNT OR, MORE LIKELY, ATTITUDE. IF AN HONOR IS IMPOSSIBLE OR UNLIKELY, THE SIGNAL IS COUNT, OTHERWISE, ATTITUDE. DON'T WORRY, YOU'LL WORK IT OUT. IF NOT, PARTNER WILL ALWAYS TELL YOU HOW YOU SHOULD HAVE KNOWN. WHEN IN DOUBT ASSUME ATTITUDE.

(5) FOUR SEVENS

Both sides vulnerable
Dealer South

North
♠ Q 10 9
♡ J 8
◇ A K 8 6 5
♣ K 3 2

East (you)
♠ K J 7 5
♡ 7 3
◇ 7 3
♣ Q J 8 7 6

South	West	North	East
1 ♠	2 ♡	3 ◇	Pass
3 ♠	Pass	4 ♠	All Pass

Opening lead: ♡ Q (Shows A K Q and asks for count)

Partner continues with the king and ace of hearts dummy ruffing with the ♠ 10.
1. Do you overruff? If so, what do you return?
2. If not, what do you discard?

FOUR SEVENS   (Solution)

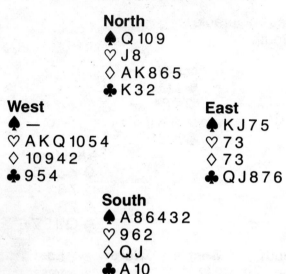

North
♠ Q 10 9
♡ J 8
◇ A K 8 6 5
♣ K 3 2

West
♠ —
♡ A K Q 10 5 4
◇ 10 9 4 2
♣ 9 5 4

East
♠ K J 7 5
♡ 7 3
◇ 7 3
♣ Q J 8 7 6

South
♠ A 8 6 4 3 2
♡ 9 6 2
◇ Q J
♣ A 10

Discard a diamond! By not overruffing you ensure yourself two trump tricks—check the spots.

KEY LESSON POINTERS

1. DON'T ALWAYS JUMP AT THE CHANCE TO OVER-RUFF DECLARER OR DUMMY WITH A RELA-TIVELY STRONG TRUMP HOLDING. BY NOT OVERRUFFING YOU MAY MAKE AN ADDITIONAL TRICK.
2. WHEN YOU DECIDE NOT TO OVERRUFF AND THERE IS A FAINT CHANCE OF AN EVENTUAL END PLAY OR TRUMP COUP (DECLARER SMELLS OUT THE SITUATION), DISCARD FROM YOUR SHORTER SIDE SUIT.

(6) THE SHIFT

North-South vulnerable
Dealer South

North
♠ 7 5
♡ 8 6
◇ Q 7 5
♣ A K Q 10 6 2

East (you)
♠ J 9 4
♡ A 10 5 3
◇ 10 6 3
♣ J 8 4

South	West	North	East
1 ◇	1 ♠	2 ♣	Pass
2 ◇	Pass	3 ◇	Pass
3 NT	All Pass		

Opening lead: ♠ 3

You play the ♠ J and declarer wins with the ♠ K.

1. Who has the ♠ A?
2. At trick two declarer leads the ◇ K which loses to partner's ace. At trick three partner shifts to the ♡ 2. You win the ♡ A. What do you return at trick four? Why?

THE SHIFT (Solution)

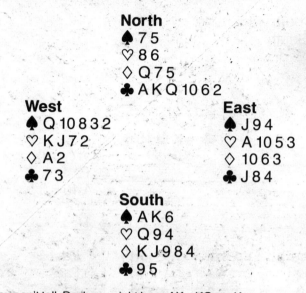

North
♠ 7 5
♡ 8 6
♦ Q 7 5
♣ A K Q 10 6 2

West
♠ Q 10 8 3 2
♡ K J 7 2
♦ A 2
♣ 7 3

East
♠ J 9 4
♡ A 10 5 3
♦ 10 6 3
♣ J 8 4

South
♠ A K 6
♡ Q 9 4
♦ K J 9 8 4
♣ 9 5

1. You can't tell. Declarer might have AKx, KQx or Kxx.
2. The ♡ 3, your original fourth best. If partner had wanted a spade return, he would have led a higher heart.

KEY LESSON POINTERS

1. WHEN HOLDING BOTH THE ACE AND KING IN THE SUIT THE OPPONENTS HAVE LED, DECLARER MAKES IT HARDER FOR THE DEFENDERS TO KNOW WHAT IS GOING ON IF THE FIRST TRICK IS WON WITH THE KING. IF DECLARER WINS WITH THE ACE, THE DEFENDERS CAN INFER HE HAS THE KING JUDGING FROM THE FAILURE TO HOLDUP.

2. WHEN PARTNER LEADS UP ONE SUIT THEN SHIFTS TO ANOTHER, THE KEY TO DETERMINING WHICH SUIT PARTNER WANTS RETURNED IS THE SIZE OF THE CARD IN THE SECOND SUIT.

   (A) IF PARTNER SHIFTS TO A LOW CARD IN THE SECOND SUIT, HE WANTS THE SECOND SUIT RETURNED.

   (B) IF PARTNER SHIFTS TO A HIGH SPOT CARD IN THE SECOND SUIT, HE WANTS THE FIRST SUIT RETURNED.

   FOR EXAMPLE, IF WEST HELD: ♠ A 10 8 3 2 ♡ J 8 7 2 ♦ A 2 ♣ 7 3 HE WOULD SHIFT TO THE ♡ 8.

3. WHEN RETURNING PARTNER'S SUIT, LEAD BACK THE HIGHER OF TWO REMAINING CARDS, AND WITH FEW EXCEPTIONS, THE LOWER OF THREE REMAINING CARDS.

(7) · WHICH SUIT?

East-West vulnerable
Dealer West

North
♠ K 4
♡ K 9 8 2
◇ K 3
♣ A 7 6 5 4

West (you)
♠ Q 10 9 6 5
♡ 3
◇ 9 4
♣ K 10 9 8 3

West	North	East	South
Pass	1 ♣	3 ◇	3 ♠
Pass	3 NT	Pass	4 ♡
All Pass			

Opening lead: ◇ 9

Partner wins the first two tricks with the ◇ Q and ◇ A, declarer playing the ◇ J and the ◇ 2.

Partner switches to the ♡ Q which declarer wins in his own hand. At trick four declarer leads a low heart:

1. What do you think declarer's original distribution was?
2. What do you think partner has in hearts?
3. What do you discard?

WHICH SUIT?   (Solution)

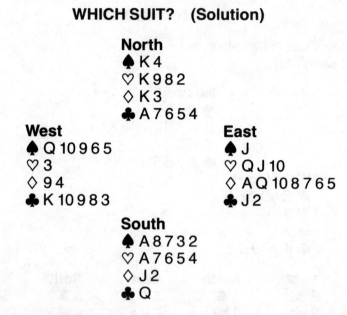

North
♠ K 4
♡ K 9 8 2
◇ K 3
♣ A 7 6 5 4

West
♠ Q 10 9 6 5
♡ 3
◇ 9 4
♣ K 10 9 8 3

East
♠ J
♡ Q J 10
◇ A Q 10 8 7 6 5
♣ J 2

South
♠ A 8 7 3 2
♡ A 7 6 5 4
◇ J 2
♣ Q

1. 5-5-2-1 judging from the bidding and partner's return.
2. Q J 10. Partner is not leading a heart, exposing himself to a possible finesse without a perfect sequence.
3. A low club. It is a question of entries. If you discard a spade, declarer has the hand entries to establish the fifth spade. However, if you discard a club, declarer does not have enough dummy entries to establish the fifth club.

KEY LESSON POINTERS

1. IN GENERAL, DEFENDERS SHOULD KEEP LENGTH PARITY WITH THE DUMMY WHEN DISCARDING. HOWEVER, IT IS ALSO IMPORTANT TO KEEP LENGTH PARITY WITH THE DECLARER. WHEN FORCED TO GIVE UP LENGTH PARITY WITH ONE HAND OR THE OTHER IT MAY BECOME A MATTER OF ENTRIES.
2. WHEN PARTNER LEADS A TRUMP HONOR, ASSUME A PERFECT SEQUENCE.
3. VULNERABLE PREEMPTS VS. NON-VULNERABLE OPPONENTS GENERALLY SHOW REASONABLE HANDS WITH SELF-RESPECTING SUITS.

(8)   STRONG RAISE

East-West vulnerable
Dealer South

North
♠ 10 6 3
♡ Q 7 5
◇ Q J 8 5
♣ A J 10

West (you)
♠ A K J 7
♡ K 6 3
◇ 4
♣ 7 6 4 3 2

South	West	North	East
1 ♡	1 ♠	2 ♡	2 ♠
3 ♡	All Pass		

Opening lead: ♠ K

1. Partner plays the ♠ 9, declarer the ♠ 2. What does partner's play mean?
2. What do you play at trick two?
3. You shift to your singleton diamond, dummy plays low, partner the ◇ 10 and declarer the ◇ A. Who has the ◇ K?
4. At trick three declarer plays the ♡ A, partner playing the ♡ 2, and continues with the ♡ 10. Which heart do you play? Why?
5. You rise with your ♡ K, and partner plays the ♡ 8. What do you play now?

STRONG RAISE   (Solution)

North
♠ 10 6 3
♡ Q 7 5
◇ Q J 8 5
♣ A J 10

West
♠ A K J 7
♡ K 6 3
◇ 4
♣ 7 6 4 3 2

East
♠ Q 9 5 4
♡ 8 2
◇ 10 7 6 3
♣ K 9 8

South
♠ 8 2
♡ A J 10 9 4
◇ A K 9 2
♣ Q 5

1. It shows an equal honor. In this case the ♠ Q. It is not a count signal.
2. Your singleton diamond.
3. Declarer. If not, he would have played an honor from dummy.
4. The ♡ K. You are still trying for a diamond ruff, aren't you?
5. A low spade to partner's ♠ Q. Partner gives you a diamond ruff and the ♣ K is the setting trick.

KEY LESSON POINTERS

1. WHEN PARTNER LEADS A KING IN A SUPPORTED SUIT VS. A SUIT CONTRACT, ASSUMING KING FROM ACE-KING, THIRD HAND SIGNALS COUNT ONLY IF THE QUEEN OR THE AJ APPEAR IN DUMMY, OTHERWISE ATTITUDE.
2. SHORT SUIT LEADS AND SHORT SUIT SWITCHES WORK BEST WHEN THE PLAYER LOOKING FOR A RUFF HAS A TRUMP ENTRY.
3. IT PAYS TO CONSERVE PARTNER'S ENTRY UNTIL YOU HAVE VOIDED YOURSELF. THEN, WHEN YOU GET IN WITH YOUR TRUMP HONOR, YOU CAN PUT PARTNER IN TO GET YOUR CHERISHED RUFF.

(9) STAYING WITH IT

North
♠ 10 9 5 4
♡ K 9 7 3
♢ K J 10
♣ A 2

East (you)
♠ K J 7 6
♡ 2
♢ 9 7 4 3 2
♣ J 8 4

South	West	North	East
2 NT*	Pass	3 ♣	Pass
3 ♡	Pass	4 ♣**	Pass
4 ♢***	Pass	6 ♡	All Pass

   * 20-22
  ** Key Card Blackwood
*** 0 or 3 Aces

Opening lead: ♣ 10

1. Declarer wins with the ♣ K, which club do you play?
2. Declarer draws trumps in three rounds, partner having J 10x. Assuming you want to tell your partner you have nothing in diamonds as well as the count in diamonds, how would you go about it?
3. Declarer continues by playing three rounds of diamonds ending in dummy, partner having started with a small doubleton. On the third diamond partner discards the ♣ 3. What does that mean?
4. Declarer plays the ♣ A, underplaying the ♣ Q from his hand. What was declarer's original distribution?
5. The ♠ 10 is led from the dummy. Which spade do you play, why?

STAYING WITH IT   (Solution)

North
♠ 10 9 5 4
♡ K 9 7 3
♢ K J 10
♣ A 2

West
♠ Q 2
♡ J 10 5
♢ 8 5
♣ 10 9 7 6 5 3

East
♠ K J 7 6
♡ 2
♢ 9 7 4 3 2
♣ J 8 4

South
♠ A 8 3
♡ A Q 8 6 4
♢ A Q 6
♣ K Q

1. The ♣ 4.
2. The ♢ 2, attitude, followed by the ♢ 9, (or ♢ 7) present count.
3. Partner is also giving present count. His discard of his lowest club indicates an odd number of clubs at the time of the discard.
4. Declarer is known to have started with five hearts, three diamonds, and two clubs. Therefore, three spades.
5. Low! Declarer has already turned up with 17 high card points so he cannot have the ♠ A Q. Besides, in order to defeat the contract you must find partner with ♠ Qx and you must not block the suit by covering.

KEY LESSON POINTERS

1. AFTER EITHER DEFENDER LEADS AN HONOR CARD, THE FIRST DISCARD IN THE SUIT IS USUALLY PRESENT COUNT. PRESENT COUNT MEANS DISCARDING YOUR LOWEST CARD WITH AN ODD NUMBER OF CARDS REMAINING, AND THE HIGHEST SPOT CARD YOU CAN AFFORD WITH AN EVEN NUMBER OF CARDS REMAINING.
2. TO SHOW BOTH ATTITUDE AND COUNT IN A SUIT THAT HAS NOT BEEN PLAYED, THE FIRST DISCARD IS ATTITUDE AND THE SECOND IS PRESENT COUNT.

(10)   DOUBLING A STAYMAN RESPONSE

Both sides vulnerable
Dealer South

North
♠ K Q 9 5
♡ Q J 10 6
◇ Q 4
♣ 8 4 2

East (you)
♠ 8 6
♡ K 9 8
◇ J 3 2
♣ A K Q 9 6

South	West	North	East
1 NT	Pass	2 ♣	Dbl.
2 ♡	Pass	4 ♡	All Pass

Opening lead: ♣ 10

1. How many clubs do you think your partner has? Why?
2. You win the first three club tricks and partner discards the
    ◇ 6 on the third club. What do you play to the fourth trick?

DOUBLING A STAYMAN RESPONSE   (Solution)

North
♠ K Q 9 5
♡ Q J 10 6
♢ Q 4
♣ 8 4 2

West
♠ 10 7 4 3
♡ 7 4
♢ 10 9 8 7 6
♣ 10 3

East
♠ 8 6
♡ K 9 8
♢ J 3 2
♣ A K Q 9 6

South
♠ A J 2
♡ A 5 3 2
♢ A K 5
♣ J 7 5

1. Either a singleton or a doubleton. You know this because you can see the ♣ 9. If you couldn't, the lead could conceivably be from 10 9x.
2. Another club. Count partner's points. Between you and dummy you can see 23 high card points. Declarer has at least 15 which means partner can have at most one queen. But you can see all four queens. Poor partner, either he has the ♠ J or he is completely busted.

   But wait! Maybe he has the ♡ 7. If he does, he can uppercut dummy on the fourth club and promote your trump holding to the setting trick.

KEY LESSON POINTERS

1. WHEN AN HONOR CARD IS LED IN A SUIT YOU HAVE BID, AND THE CARD DIRECTLY BENEATH IT IN RANK IS VISIBLE, THE LEAD MUST EITHER BE A SINGLETON OR A DOUBLETON.
2. WHEN EITHER PARTNER'S OR DECLARER'S STRENGTH IS PRETTY WELL KNOWN, ADD YOUR POINTS TO DUMMY'S POINTS AND ADD THE TOTAL TO THE HAND THAT IS PRETTY WELL KNOWN. IN THAT WAY YOU CAN DISCOVER HOW STRONG THE REMAINING HAND IS.
3. WHEN THERE ARE NO TRICKS COMING FROM THE SIDES SUITS, A RUFF AND A SLUFF MIGHT BE JUST WHAT THE DOCTOR ORDERED.

(11) NEGATIVE DOUBLE

Both sides vulnerable
Dealer North

North
♠ J 2
♡ 8 2
◊ A K Q 10 7
♣ A Q 10 5

East (you)
♠ A Q 10 9 8
♡ A J 3
◊ 6 3 2
♣ 8 6

North	East	South	West
1 ◊	1 ♠	Dbl*	Pass
2 ♣	Pass	2 NT	Pass
3 NT	All Pass		

*Negative
Opening lead: ♠ 6

1. Dummy plays the jack, which spade do you play?
2. You win the ace, what do you play at trick two?

NEGATIVE DOUBLE   (Solution)

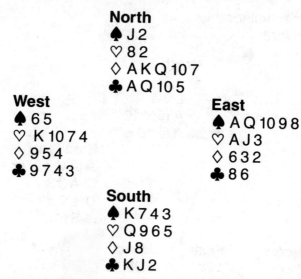

North
♠ J 2
♡ 8 2
♢ A K Q 10 7
♣ A Q 10 5

West
♠ 6 5
♡ K 10 7 4
♢ 9 5 4
♣ 9 7 4 3

East
♠ A Q 10 9 8
♡ A J 3
♢ 6 3 2
♣ 8 6

South
♠ K 7 4 3
♡ Q 9 6 5
♢ J 8
♣ K J 2

2. The ♡ J. Count tricks. From the looks of things, declarer has five diamond tricks and at least three clubs along with the ♠ K. That comes to a total of at least nine, and that is why you did not allow declarer to win the first trick.

   In order to defeat this contract you are going to have to take four heart tricks. In order to do that, partner needs at least K 10 7x. If he has that holding, you must shift to the ♡ J to realize four tricks. No other heart will work.

KEY LESSON POINTERS

1. YOU CAN NEVER START COUNTING DECLARER'S TRICKS TOO SOON, AS WITNESSED BY THIS DEAL. PLAY THE ♠ Q AT TRICK ONE AND THE CONTRACT GOES BYE-BYE.
2. HAVING ISOLATED THE SUIT YOU MUST ATTACK TO DE-FEAT THE CONTRACT, YOU SHOULD KNOW: (1) HOW MANY TRICKS YOU NEED; (2) THE LEAST PARTNER NEEDS IN THE SUIT TO GET THOSE TRICKS—THEN PLAY ACCORD-INGLY.
3. A SHIFT IN THE MIDDLE OF THE HAND DOES NOT NECES-SARILY SHOW THE EXPECTED HOLDING IN THE SUIT. FOR EXAMPLE, EAST'S SHIFT TO THE ♡ J AT TRICK TWO DOES NOT PROMISE THE ♡ 10 AS IT WOULD ON OPENING LEAD.

(12) BIG TRUMPS

North-South vulnerable
Dealer East

North
♠ 8 7 5 3
♡ A K Q
◊ 8 7 3 2
♣ A Q

East (you)
♠ 10 9
♡ 10 9 8 7
◊ A K
♣ J 6 4 3 2

East	South	West	North
Pass	Pass	1 ♠	Dbl.
1 NT	2 ◊	All Pass	

Opening lead: ♠ Q

1. Partner continues with the ♠ K and ♠ A, what do you discard?
2. At trick four partner plays the ♠ J, what do you discard this time, and why?

BIG TRUMPS   (Solution)

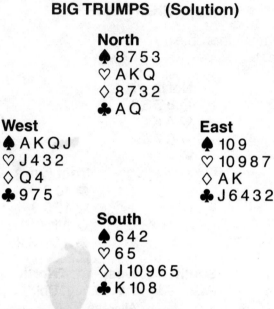

North
♠ 8 7 5 3
♡ A K Q
◇ 8 7 3 2
♣ A Q

West
♠ A K Q J
♡ J 4 3 2
◇ Q 4
♣ 9 7 5

East
♠ 10 9
♡ 10 9 8 7
◇ A K
♣ J 6 4 3 2

South
♠ 6 4 2
♡ 6 5
◇ J 10 9 6 5
♣ K 10 8

1. A low club to discourage a lead in that suit.
2. A high trump! The only tricks coming your way are trumps tricks. Why not try to make them separately? If partner has either Qx or Jxx in the trump suit, your "discard" defeats the contract.

KEY LESSON POINTERS

1. WHEN THERE ARE NO SIDE SUIT TRICKS AVAILABLE, LOOK TO THE TRUMP SUIT.
2. WHEN THERE ARE NO SIDE SUIT TRICKS AVAILABLE, RUFFING HIGH WITH THE SHORTER TRUMP HAND FREQUENTLY PROMOTES AN EQUIVALENT OR LOWER TRUMP HONOR IN PARTNER'S HAND.
3. THE FOLLOWING IS MY IDEA: I THINK THAT ON BALANCE IT IS RIGHT TO LEAD THE Q FROM A K Q VS. SUIT CONTRACTS, THIRD HAND GIVING COUNT. FURTHERMORE, I THINK THAT THE OPENING LEADER CAN ALSO GIVE HIS PARTNER COUNT!

    IF THE SECOND CARD PLAYED IS ADJACENT TO THE QUEEN (THE KING OR THE JACK) THE OPENING LEADER IS SHOWING AN EVEN NUMBER OF CARDS. IF THE SECOND CARD PLAYED IS THE ACE, THE OPENING LEADER IS SHOWING AN ODD NUMBER OF CARDS.

    THIS IN TURN ALLOWS THIRD HAND TO PLAN DISCARDS AND KNOW WHEN IT IS RIGHT TO UPPERCUT DECLARER.

    THIS SAME IDEA CAN BE USED WHEN LEADING THE K FROM KQJ COMBINATIONS OR THE Q FROM QJ10 COMBINATIONS.

(13) MISSED SLAM?

East-West vulnerable
Dealer South

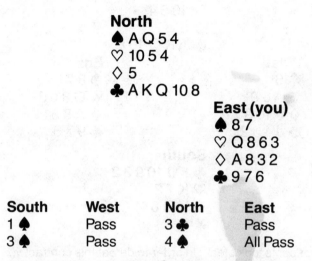

North
♠ A Q 5 4
♡ 10 5 4
◇ 5
♣ A K Q 10 8

East (you)
♠ 8 7
♡ Q 8 6 3
◇ A 8 3 2
♣ 9 7 6

South	West	North	East
1 ♠	Pass	3 ♣	Pass
3 ♠	Pass	4 ♠	All Pass

Opening lead: ◇ J (denies a higher honor)

Plan your defense.

MISSED SLAM? (Solution)

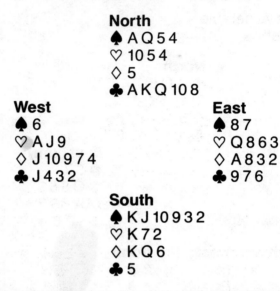

North
♠ A Q 5 4
♡ 10 5 4
◊ 5
♣ A K Q 10 8

West
♠ 6
♡ A J 9
◊ J 10 9 7 4
♣ J 4 3 2

East
♠ 8 7
♡ Q 8 6 3
◊ A 8 3 2
♣ 9 7 6

South
♠ K J 10 9 3 2
♡ K 7 2
◊ K Q 6
♣ 5

Prospects look bleak. In order to defeat this contract you must come up with three heart tricks. This isn't going to be easy as you know partner cannot have the ♡ A K and not lead one. You must find partner with specifically ♡ A J 9 and you must lead the *queen*—confidently. If declarer thinks you have the ♡ J he will duck this trick and you will have swindled declarer out of a heart trick.

It does no good to lead a low heart. Declarer will simply duck it around to his ten spot.

KEY LESSON POINTERS

1. WHEN YOU CAN SEE THAT YOU NEED A CERTAIN NUMBER OF TRICKS FROM ONE PARTICULAR SUIT, YOU MUST ASSUME PARTNER HAS THE MINIMUM AMOUNT OF STRENGTH NECESSARY TO TAKE THOSE TRICKS.
2. SOMETIMES IT IS NECESSARY TO ATTACK A SUIT WITH AN ABNORMALLY HIGH CARD TO PREVENT DECLARER FROM DUCKING THE TRICK.
3. AS THIRD HAND, WHEN YOU CAN SEE NEITHER THE ACE NOR THE KING OF A SIDE SUIT, IT IS SAFE TO ASSUME THAT THE OPENING LEADER DOES NOT OWN BOTH OF THOSE CARDS. TO A SOMEWHAT LESSER EXTENT THAT SAME ASSUMPTION CAN BE MADE WHEN YOU CAN SEE NEITHER THE KING NOR THE QUEEN OF A SIDE SUIT.

(14)   EAGLE-EYE

Both sides vulnerable
Dealer South

North
♠ Q 8
♡ 10 8 5 3
◇ K Q J 9 2
♣ 10 6

West (you)
♠ K 9 5 3
♡ 6 2
◇ A 8 4
♣ A K J 4

South	West	North	East
1 ♡	Dbl.	3 ♡	Pass
4 ♡	All Pass		

Opening lead: ♣ K

Partner plays the ♣ 5 and declarer the ♣ 7. What do you play to trick two?

EAGLE-EYE   (Solution)

North
♠ Q 8
♡ 10 8 5 3
◇ K Q J 9 2
♣ 10 6

West
♠ K 9 5 3
♡ 6 2
◇ A 8 4
♣ A K J 4

East
♠ 7 6 4
♡ 7 4
◇ 7 6 5 3
♣ Q 5 3 2

South
♠ A J 10 2
♡ A K Q J 9
◇ 10
♣ 9 8 7

The ♣ 4. Partner's ♣ 5 is a relatively high card. Whenever there are two lower cards missing, it can be presumed that partner is interested in the suit you have led. As the only missing honor is the queen, partner figures to have it (unless he has a doubleton). Best chance to defeat the contract is to lead a low club at trick two. Partner returns a spade before your ◇ A is driven out, and you collect four tricks—two clubs, one spade, and one diamond.

Had partner played a low club at trick one, your best chance would be to shift to a low spade hoping declarer has the A 10 and misguesses. You must try to build up a spade winner before diamonds become established.

KEY LESSON POINTERS

1. IT IS NOT THE SIZE OF THE CARD THAT PARTNER PLAYS THAT DETERMINES WHETHER OR NOT IT IS A SIGNAL, IT IS THE *RELATIVE* SIZE. TO DETERMINE THE RELATIVE SIZE, LOOK TO SEE HOW MANY LOWER CARDS ARE NOT VISIBLE. IF ONE IS MISSING, PARTNER MAY OR MAY NOT BE SIGNALLING ENCOURAGEMENT, IF TWO OR MORE ARE MISSING, PARTNER IS ALMOST ALWAYS SIGNALLING ENCOURAGEMENT.

2. WHEN AN ACTIVE DEFENSE IS REQUIRED, IT MIGHT WELL BE THAT THE SUIT THAT MUST BE PLAYED HAS TO BE ATTACKED FROM ONE PARTICULAR SIDE. IF THAT IS THE CASE, CERTAIN SCARY UNDERLEADS MAY BE IN ORDER. COURAGE.

(15) MANY QUESTIONS

North
♠ 6 4
♡ A Q 3
♢ 6 4 2
♣ Q J 10 9 8

West (you)
♠ A K 3 2
♡ J 7 6
♢ J 10 9 8
♣ K 5

South	West	North	East
1 NT	Pass	3 NT	All Pass

Opening lead: ♢ J

Partner plays the ♢ 3 and declarer the ♢ K. At trick two the ♡ 4 is led to dummy's queen, partner playing the ♡ 10. At trick three the ♣ Q is played, partner playing the ♣ 2. Question time.

1. How may points does declarer have in diamonds?
2. What does the ♡ 10 mean?
3. How many clubs does partner have?
4. Is there any reason to duck this trick?
5. Assuming you win the trick, what do you play next?

MANY QUESTIONS   (Solution)

North
♠ 6 4
♡ A Q 3
◇ 6 4 2
♣ Q J 10 9 8

West
♠ A K 3 2
♡ J 7 6
◇ J 10 9 8
♣ K 5

East
♠ Q J 5
♡ 10 9 8 5
◇ 7 5 3
♣ 7 6 2

South
♠ 10 9 8 7
♡ K 4 2
◇ A K Q
♣ A 4 3

1. Nine. Judging from partner's failure to signal. Remember, partner's play at trick one is attitude, not count.
2. Top of a sequence. When the opponents start a suit and fourth hand plays an honor card unnecessarily, it shows the same card that would have been led had that player been on lead.
3. Three.
4. Not really. If you could somehow remove the ace of hearts (you can't) you could duck this trick, win the second club and knock out the ace of hearts while the clubs are blocked. Of course, this means baring your ♣ K without breaking out in a cold sweat.
5. A small spade. You need four spade tricks and partner is marked with the ♠ Q. (Declarer has already turned up with 16 points). Lead low to avoid a block in case partner has ♠ Q Jx.

KEY LESSON POINTERS

1. YOU MUST HAVE IT CLEAR IN YOU OWN MIND WHEN PARTNER'S SIGNALS ARE ATTITUDE AND WHEN THEY ARE COUNT. IN GENERAL, WHEN YOU LEAD AN HONOR CARD, PARTNER GIVES YOU ATTITUDE. WHEN THEY LEAD THE SUIT FIRST, PARTNER GIVES COUNT.
2. HONOR DISCARDS OR HONOR PLAYS BY SECOND OR FOURTH HAND GENERALLY SHOW SEQUENCES. A GOOD RULE IS TO HAVE THE HONOR CARD SHOW THE SAME CARD THAT WOULD HAVE BEEN LED.

(16) DECISIONS

North-South vulnerable
Dealer North

North
♠ A K Q 4
♡ 3 2
◇ Q J 9 7 6
♣ 3 2

West (you)
♠ 2
♡ Q
◇ A K 10 2
♣ K J 10 9 8 7 6

North	East	South	West
1 ◇	2 ♡*	2 ♠	4 ♣
4 ♠	5 ♣	5 ♠	Dbl.
All Pass			

*Weak

Opening lead; ◇K

1. Partner plays the ◇8 and declarer the ◇4, what do you play to trick two?
2. You continue with the ◇A and both partner and the declarer follow. What do you play to trick three?

DECISIONS   (Solution)

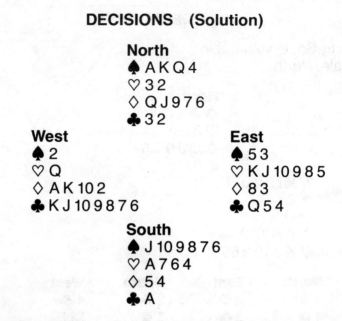

North
♠ A K Q 4
♡ 3 2
◇ Q J 9 7 6
♣ 3 2

West
♠ 2
♡ Q
◇ A K 10 2
♣ K J 10 9 8 7 6

East
♠ 5 3
♡ K J 10 9 8 5
◇ 8 3
♣ Q 5 4

South
♠ J 10 9 8 7 6
♡ A 7 6 4
◇ 5 4
♣ A

A third diamond to kill one of dummy's discards. You have a reasonable count on the hand from the bidding. Partner is known to have two diamonds, six hearts for his weak jump overcall, and probably three clubs. This means that declarer is 6-4-2-1. If you kill just one of declarer's discards he cannot possibly come to 11 tricks unless he started with both the ♡ A K and partner has the ♣ A.

Count declarer's tricks. He has six spades in his hand and can get two diamond discards for eight. If he has the ♣ A he can discard two hearts but must lose one heart trick if partner has either the ace or the king.

Even if declarer has a losing club, what matter? He can discard a club and a heart on the diamonds but still must lose one heart trick. Notice, if you don't play three rounds of diamonds at once the hand is an easy make.

KEY LESSON POINTERS

1. TRY TO WORK OUT THE DISTRIBUTION FROM THE BIDDING BEFORE MAKING ANY "BIG" PLAYS.
2. THE SUREST WAY TO KNOW WHAT IS GOING ON IS TO COUNT DECLARER'S TRICKS.
3. KILLING A DISCARD IS A DEFENSIVE STRATAGEM OFTEN OVERLOOKED.
4. DON'T PLAY PARTNER FOR MUCH OF A HAND WHEN HE PREEMPTS AT FAVORABLE VULNERABILITY. IF YOU FIND ONE DEFENSIVE TRICK CONSIDER YOURSELF FORTUNATE.

(17) STRANDED WINNER

East-West vulnerable
Dealer North

North
♠ Q 9 2
♡ J
◇ A K 3 2
♣ Q J 8 7 6

West (you)
♠ J 5 3
♡ A 6 2
◇ Q J 10 9 4
♣ 5 2

North	East	South	West
1 ♣	Pass	1 ♡	Pass
1 NT	Pass	3 ♡	All Pass

Opening lead: ◇ Q

Dummy wins as declarer discards the ♠ 4. Declarer leads the ♡ J, partner playing the ♡ 5 and declarer the ♡ 3.
1. Do you win this trick? If so, what do you return?
   You win the trick and shift to the ♣ 5. Dummy plays low, partner's ♣ 9 forcing out the ♣ K. Declarer leads the ♡ 9 to partner's king, dummy discarding a diamond. Partner plays the ♣ A and ♣ 10, declarer following, and you ruff.
2. What is declarer's distribution?
3. What do you play at this point?

STRANDED WINNER (Solution)

North
♠ Q 9 2
♡ J
◇ A K 3 2
♣ Q J 8 7 6

West
♠ J 5 3
♡ A 6 2
◇ Q J 10 9 4
♣ 5 2

East
♠ K 7 6
♡ K 8 5
◇ 8 7 6 5
♣ A 10 9

South
♠ A 10 8 4
♡ Q 10 9 7 4 3
◇ —
♣ K 4 3

Declarer must be 4-6-0-3. If partner had ♡Kx he would have covered the ♡J. Therefore, declarer cannot have seven hearts. His jump rebid promised six.

Your proper return is a diamond. Let declarer discard another spade. He will still remain with two spades and partner can ruff if a club is led from the table.

As partner is marked with a spade honor, your diamond return ensures a one trick set regardless of what that honor is. If you return a spade, and declarer is clever enough to play the ♠9, you have just chewed up the setting trick.

KEY LESSON POINTERS

1. WHEN DUMMY COMES DOWN WITH FEWER TRUMPS THAN DECLARER IS EXPECTING, DON'T BE DUCKING TRICKS IN THE TRUMP SUIT. PARTNER'S TRUMPS MAY BE STRONGER THAN YOU SUSPECT.
2. WHEN DECLARER LEAVES A STRANDED WINNER IN DUMMY, THE INFERENCE IS THAT HE DOESN'T NEED THE IMMEDIATE DISCARD.
3. THE SECRET TO MOST GOOD DEFENSIVE PLAYS IS COUNTING.

(18)   HOW TO DO IT

North-South vulnerable
Dealer West

                    North
                    ♠ K 9 6
                    ♡ K 4
                    ◇ K Q 9
                    ♣ A Q 6 5 4
    West (you)
    ♠ Q 2
    ♡ J 9 7
    ◇ A 10 6 5 4
    ♣ J 10 7

West	**North**	**East**	**South**
Pass	1 NT	2 ♠	4 ♡
All Pass			

Opening lead: ♠ Q

Dummy plays low, partner plays the ♠ 8, and declarer follows with the ♠ 3. What do you play to trick two?

HOW TO DO IT   (Solution)

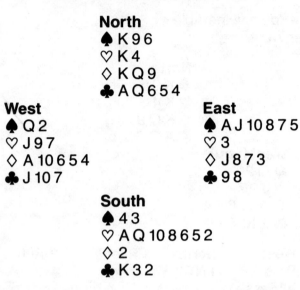

North
♠ K 9 6
♡ K 4
♢ K Q 9
♣ A Q 6 5 4

West
♠ Q 2
♡ J 9 7
♢ A 10 6 5 4
♣ J 10 7

East
♠ A J 10 8 7 5
♡ 3
♢ J 8 7 3
♣ 9 8

South
♠ 4 3
♡ A Q 10 8 6 5 2
♢ 2
♣ K 3 2

The ♢ A. You have this hand defeated if declarer has at least one diamond and one more spade—that's all you need.

Cash the ♢ A and lead your remaining spade. Partner wins and continues the suit promoting your jack of hearts to the setting trick. If spades are continued at tricks two and three, declarer discards a diamond on the third spade and claims the balance.

KEY LESSON POINTERS

1. WHEN TRYING TO PROMOTE A TRUMP TRICK BY MEANS OF AN OVERRUFF, CASH YOUR SIDE WINNER(S) FIRST. DECLARER MAY BE ABLE TO DISCARD A LOSER (RATHER THAN RUFF) IF YOU DON'T.
2. WHEN VISUALIZING A WINNING DEFENSE, DO SO BY GIVING YOUR PARTNER THE LEAST AMOUNT OF HIGH CARD STRENGTH NECESSARY.
3. OVERCALLS OF ONE NOTRUMP OPENING BIDS GENERALLY SHOW GOOD SUITS BUT NOT NECESSARILY GOOD HANDS. THEY OFTEN LOOK LIKE WEAK TWO BIDS.

(19)   NO CHOICE

East-West vulnerable
Dealer North

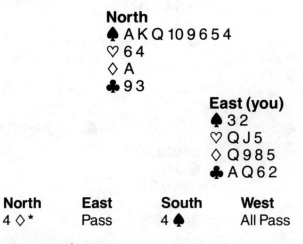

North
♠ A K Q 10 9 6 5 4
♡ 6 4
◇ A
♣ 9 3

East (you)
♠ 3 2
♡ Q J 5
◇ Q 9 8 5
♣ A Q 6 2

North	East	South	West
4 ◇ *	Pass	4 ♠	All Pass

*Strong 4 ♠ opening
Opening lead: ♣ J (denies a higher honor)

1. You play the ace, what do you return at trick two?
2. You play the ♡ Q which holds, declarer playing the ♡ 2 and partner the ♡ 7. What do you play to trick three?

NO CHOICE (Solution)

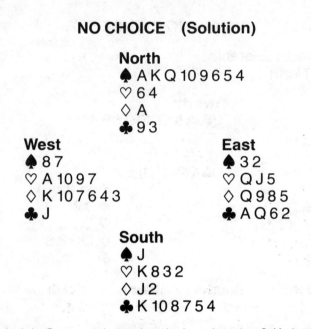

North
♠ A K Q 10 9 6 5 4
♡ 6 4
◇ A
♣ 9 3

West
♠ 8 7
♡ A 10 9 7
◇ K 10 7 6 4 3
♣ J

East
♠ 3 2
♡ Q J 5
◇ Q 9 8 5
♣ A Q 6 2

South
♠ J
♡ K 8 3 2
◇ J 2
♣ K 10 8 7 5 4

A club. Once you know that declarer has the ♣ K, there is little hope to defeat the contract unless partner has both a singleton ♣ and the ♡ A.

If you give your partner an immediate club ruff at trick two, you won't be able to organize two heart tricks. Declarer ducks, partner ruffs, but cannot prevent declarer from discarding a heart upon the ♣ K. (The ♠ J is the entry to the South hand).

The fact that partner has given you the ♡ 7 should not deter you. (1) It may have been his lowest heart—(it was)—(2) you are still trying to defeat this contract, remember?

KEY LESSON POINTERS

1. ASSUME THE CONTRACT CAN BE DEFEATED. GIVE PARTNER AS LITTLE OR AS MUCH AS IS NECESSARY AND PLAY FOR IT.
2. DO NOT BE TAKEN IN BY THE SIZE OF PARTNER'S SPOT CARD WHEN TRYING TO DETERMINE WHETHER OR NOT IT IS A POSITIVE SIGNAL. CONSIDER THE RELATIVE SIZE OF THE CARD. IN OTHER WORDS, HOW MANY LOWER CARDS ARE VISIBLE? USING THIS CRITERIA, A SEVEN MAY WELL BE A LOW CARD (IF ALL THE LOWER ONES ARE VISIBLE), AND A FOUR MAY BE A HIGH CARD IF NEITHER THE DEUCE NOR THE TREY ARE VISIBLE).

(20)   WHAT'S UP?

North-South vulnerable
Dealer East

North
♠ 10 2
♡ 7 6
◊ 6 2
♣ A K Q J 9 8 7

West (you)
♠ K J 3
♡ A 8 5
◊ Q J 9 8 7
♣ 6 5

East	South	West	North
Pass	1 ♡	2 ◊	3 ♣
3 ◊	4 ♡	All Pass	

Opening lead: ◊ Q

Partner overtakes with the ◊K which holds the trick. At trick two partner returns the ♡2. Declarer plays the ♡Q.
1. Do you win this trick? If so, what do you return?

WHAT'S UP?   (Solution)

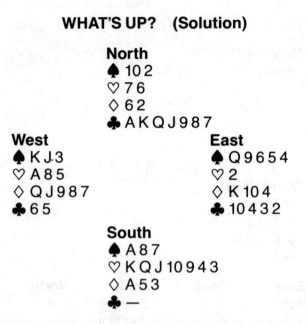

North
♠ 10 2
♡ 7 6
♢ 6 2
♣ A K Q J 9 8 7

West
♠ K J 3
♡ A 8 5
♢ Q J 9 8 7
♣ 6 5

East
♠ Q 9 6 5 4
♡ 2
♢ K 10 4
♣ 10 4 3 2

South
♠ A 8 7
♡ K Q J 10 9 4 3
♢ A 5 3
♣ —

Your moment of truth has arrived. Do you trust your partner or not? Looking at those clubs how could he return a trump unless he thought declarer was void?

If his assessment is correct then it is imperative that you win the ♡A and return the ♡8. Very important that ♡8, otherwise declarer can get to dummy with the ♡7! Your defense defeats the contract two tricks. Any other defense allows the declarer to make an overtrick.

KEY LESSON POINTERS

1. WHEN PARTNER PLAYS A TRUMP IN THE FACE OF A LONG SIDE SUIT IN DUMMY, HE EITHER CONTROLS THE SUIT, OR KNOWS THAT DECLARER CANNOT USE THE SUIT.
2. WHEN A KING IS ALLOWED TO HOLD AN EARLY LEAD AND THERE IS A DOUBLETON IN THE DUMMY, THERE IS A GOOD CHANCE THAT DECLARER HOLDS THE ACE AND IS RETAINING CONTROL OF THE SUIT WITH THE IDEA OF RUFFING A THIRD ROUND IN THE DUMMY.
3. WHEN TRYING TO KEEP DECLARER FROM GETTING TO DUMMY, DON'T GET CARELESS WHEN LEADING TRUMPS. MAKE SURE THE TRUMP YOU PLAY IS HIGHER THAN DUMMY'S REMAINING TRUMP, PARTICULARLY WHEN PARTNER IS MARKED WITH SHORT TRUMPS ON THE BIDDING.

(21) DESERTION

North-South vulnerable
Dealer East

<pre>
              North
              ♠ 6
              ♡ 8 4 3
              ◇ K J 10 9 8 7
              ♣ A 7 6
                           East (you)
                           ♠ A 5 2
                           ♡ K Q J 7
                           ◇ 3
                           ♣ Q J 9 4 2
</pre>

East	South	West	North
1 ♣	Dbl.	Pass	2 ◇
2 ♡	2 ♠	Pass	3 ◇
Pass	3 NT	All Pass	

Opening lead: ♣ 3

Declarer wins in dummy and plays the ♠ 6.

1. Can you see any reason to win this trick? If so, what do you return at trick three?

DESERTION   (Solution)

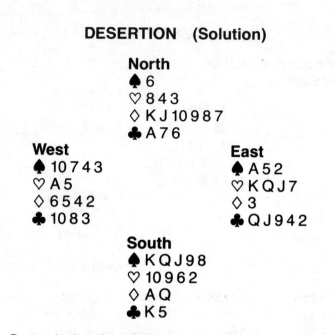

North
- ♠ 6
- ♡ 8 4 3
- ◇ K J 10 9 8 7
- ♣ A 7 6

West
- ♠ 10 7 4 3
- ♡ A 5
- ◇ 6 5 4 2
- ♣ 10 8 3

East
- ♠ A 5 2
- ♡ K Q J 7
- ◇ 3
- ♣ Q J 9 4 2

South
- ♠ K Q J 9 8
- ♡ 10 9 6 2
- ◇ A Q
- ♣ K 5

Dummy's play of the ♣ A should arouse your suspicions. Why would declarer remove the entry to dummy's diamond suit unless his diamonds were solid? He wouldn't.

You can count tricks. Declarer has six diamond tricks and surely the king of clubs for a total of 8. If declarer has the ♡ A the hand cannot be defeated. You must play partner for that card. Furthermore, you must be careful about not blocking the suit in case partner has the doubleton ace. Your play is to win the ♠ A and play the ♡ 7. Leave the rest to partner.

KEY LESSON POINTERS

1. WHEN DECLARER LEAVES AN APPARENT STRONG SUIT IN DUMMY ENTRYLESS, ASSUME HE HAS THE MISSING HONORS IN THE SUIT.
2. YOU MUST BE ALERT TO DECLARER'S STEALING A NINTH TRICK AS EARLY AS TRICK TWO. THEREFORE, START YOUR TRICK COUNTING IMMEDIATELY. EASIER WHEN THE DUMMY HAS THE LONG SUIT, OF COURSE.
3. WHEN PARTNER NEEDS A SPECIFIC HONOR CARD TO DEFEAT THE CONTRACT, PLAY HIM FOR IT. FURTHERMORE, ASSUMING HE HAS THAT CARD, AVOID BLOCKING THE SUIT IN CASE THE HONOR IS DOUBLETON.

(22) THE STRIP

East-West vulnerable
Dealer North

>   **North**
>   ♠ 10 7 5
>   ♡ K Q
>   ◊ Q J 8 4 2
>   ♣ K 7 6
>
> **West (you)**
> ♠ K J 8 6 3
> ♡ 10 7 6
> ◊ 9
> ♣ Q J 10 4

North	East	South	West
Pass	Pass	1 ◊	Pass
3 ◊	Pass	6 ◊	All Pass

Opening lead: ♣ Q

Declarer wins the ♣ A, leads a diamond to the queen, partner playing the ◊ 10, cashes the ♣ K and ruffs a club. He continues with the ace and a heart. Are you counting?

At this point a low spade is led from dummy. Partner plays the ♠ 2 and declarer the ♠ A. Declarer exits with the ♠ 9.

1. What is declarer's distribution?
2. Which spade do you play?

THE STRIP   (Solution)

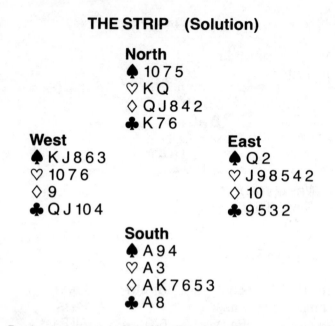

North
- ♠ 10 7 5
- ♡ K Q
- ◊ Q J 8 4 2
- ♣ K 7 6

West
- ♠ K J 8 6 3
- ♡ 10 7 6
- ◊ 9
- ♣ Q J 10 4

East
- ♠ Q 2
- ♡ J 9 8 5 4 2
- ◊ 10
- ♣ 9 5 3 2

South
- ♠ A 9 4
- ♡ A 3
- ◊ A K 7 6 5 3
- ♣ A 8

Declarer must be 3-2-6-2. This you know whether or not partner is giving you count signals. Declarer cannot have three hearts and play this way nor would he leave any low trumps outstanding. (Not to mention that your partner has played the highest remaining trump indicating he has no more). So much for declarer's distribution.

Play the ♠ K! Declarer is marked with three spades headed by the ace. He cannot logically have ♠ A Qx and play this way. Therefore he must have Axx and partner's queen is bare. If you play the jack, partner must win and concede a ruff and a sluff allowing declarer to discard his remaining spade.

KEY LESSON POINTERS

1. WHEN PARTNER PLAYS THE HIGHEST MISSING TRUMP, ASSUME HE HAS NO MORE.
2. YOU DON'T NEED COUNT SIGNALS FROM PARTNER ON EVERY HAND TO WORK OUT DECLARER'S DISTRIBUTION.
3. WHEN A HAND IS BEING STRIPPED ASSUME DECLARER IS PLAYING LOGICALLY AND PLAY ACCORDINGLY.
4. COUNT, COUNT, COUNT, COUNT,—AND THEN COUNT SOME MORE.

(23) DOUBLE FIT

Both sides vulnerable
Dealer South

                        North
                        ♠ 7 6 5
                        ♡ A K J 9 2
                        ◇ Q 6
                        ♣ J 10 8
        West (you)
        ♠ J 8 3 2
        ♡ 7 6
        ◇ K 10 3
        ♣ A K Q 9

South	**West**	**North**	**East**
1 ♠	Pass	2 ♡	Pass
3 ♡	Pass	3 ♠	Pass
4 ♠	All Pass		

Opening lead: ♣ Q*

*Asking for count if partner can either see the ♣ J or suspects that you are leading from A K Q.

1. Partner plays the ♣ 6 and declarer the ♣ 4. You continue with the ♣ K and partner plays the ♣ 5 and declarer the ♣ 2. What do you think partner has in clubs?
2. What do you play to trick three? Why?
3. You play a third club which declarer ruffs. His next play is the ♠ A felling partner's ♠ Q and he continues with the ♠ 10. What is your plan?

DOUBLE FIT   (Solution)

North
♠ 7 6 5
♡ A K J 9 2
◇ Q 6
♣ J 10 8

West
♠ J 8 3 2
♡ 7 6
◇ K 10 3
♣ A K Q 9

East
♠ Q
♡ 10 5 4
◇ 9 8 7 4 2
♣ 7 6 5 3

South
♠ A K 10 9 4
♡ Q 8 3
◇ A J 5
♣ 4 2

1. Partner should be high-lowing to show four clubs. It is unlikely that he has a doubleton.
2. Continue with a high club, forcing declarer to ruff, thus reducing him to your trump length.
3. Declarer is marked with both the ◇ A and the ♡ Q. (If partner has either of those cards, declarer has no chance). Your problem is to get a diamond trick without allowing declarer to discard his diamond losers on dummy's hearts.

   The answer is to duck this trick! If you win, declarer takes the rest quite easily. But what happens if you duck? If declarer plays the king and a spade, you win and cash a club. If declarer plays on hearts, you ruff the third round and exit with a trump, eventually making your king of diamonds. If declarer cashes the ♠ K and begins on hearts, you ruff the third round and exit with a club, eventually scoring the ◇ K. By ducking the ♠ 10 you retain control of the heart suit.

KEY LESSON POINTERS

1. HOLDING FOUR TRUMPS THE BEST DEFENSE IS USUALLY TO TRY TO FORCE DECLARER DOWN TO YOUR SIZE.
2. WHEN PLAYING THE FORCING GAME, IT IS SOMETIMES NECESSARY TO DUCK A TRUMP WINNER UNTIL THE DUMMY IS VOID IN TRUMPS.

(24)   RIGHT AND LEFT

North-South vulnerable
Dealer West

North
♠ 10 7 4 3
♡ 9 8
◇ A 10 9 4
♣ 8 7 4

West (you)
♠ 2
♡ A 4 3 2
◇ 8 7 6 3 2
♣ Q 10 9

West	North	East	South
Pass	Pass	1 ♠	Dbl.
Pass	2 ◇	Pass	2 ♡
All Pass			

Opening lead: ♠ 2

Partner wins the first trick with the ♠ A and continues with the ♠ K and ♠ 9. Declarer plays the ♠ 5, 8, and Q. You ruff the third ♠.

1. Why do you think your partner won the first trick with the ♠ A rather than the more conventional ♠ K?
2. What do you discard on the second spade?
3. Assume you discard the ◇ 2, what do you return after ruffing?
4. Assume you return a diamond which is ducked to partner's king, declarer playing the ◇ Q. Partner returns the ♠ J which declarer ruffs with the ♡ 7. What do you do?
5. You discard another diamond and declarer plays the ♡ Q. Now what?

RIGHT AND LEFT   (Solution)

North
♠ 10 7 4 3
♡ 9 8
◇ A 10 9 4
♣ 8 7 4

West
♠ 2
♡ A 4 3 2
◇ 8 7 6 3 2
♣ Q 10 9

East
♠ A K J 9 6
♡ 10 5
◇ K 5
♣ 6 5 3 2

South
♠ Q 8 5
♡ K Q J 7 6
◇ Q J
♣ A K J

1. There are at least four reasons why partner might win the first trick with the ace rather than the king.
   - (a) He may wish to conceal the king, hoping declarer will place the honor with the opening leader. (Not the case here).
   - (b) He might have a doubleton A K. (Also not the case here).
   - (c) He might be trying to make a suit preference play.
   - (d) He might be planning to switch to a singleton and he doesn't want you returning your original lead.
5. Win the ♡ A and return another diamond killing dummy's diamonds. The best declarer can do is play a third diamond but partner ruffs. True, declarer can overruff and enter dummy with a trump, but so what? You are now out of diamonds as well. Declarer is reduced to the club finesse. Alas, it has been a very bad year for finesses and this hand is no exception.

KEY LESSON POINTERS

1. WHEN A GOOD PARTNER PLAYS EQUAL HONORS OUT OF ORDER HE IS SENDING A MESSAGE.
2. WHEN THERE ARE NO SIDE ENTRIES TO DUMMY, LEADING DUMMY'S LENGTH BEFORE TRUMPS HAVE BEEN REMOVED IS ONE WAY OF SEVERING COMMUNICATIONS BETWEEN DECLARER AND DUMMY.

(25) CURTAINS

Both sides vulnerable
Dealer South

North
♠ Q 9 4 2
♡ 10 6 2
◇ J 6 2
♣ A Q 3

East (you)
♠ K 10 8
♡ J 9 8
◇ 10 9 3
♣ K J 6 2

South	**West**	**North**	**East**
1 NT	Pass	3 NT	All Pass

Opening lead: ♡ 5

Dummy plays low and your eight drives out declarer's king. At trick two declarer leads the ◇4 to dummy's jack, partner playing the eight.

At trick three the ♠Q is led from the dummy. Which spade do you play, and worse, why?

CURTAINS   (Solution)

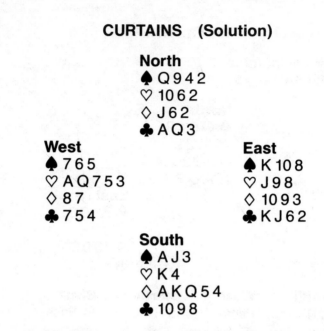

North
♠ Q 9 4 2
♡ 10 6 2
◇ J 6 2
♣ A Q 3

West
♠ 7 6 5
♡ A Q 7 5 3
◇ 8 7
♣ 7 5 4

East
♠ K 10 8
♡ J 9 8
◇ 10 9 3
♣ K J 6 2

South
♠ A J 3
♡ K 4
◇ A K Q 5 4
♣ 10 9 8

Low. Fortunately, you have vital information in two suits before having to commit at trick three. The rule of 11 tells you that declarer has only one heart higher than the ♡ 5. After his play of the ♡ K, declarer is wide open in hearts.

Partner's play of the ◇ 8 must be count. If he had a winning diamond he would have grabbed it and cashed his heart winners. If it is count, declarer has five diamonds to go along with one heart and two black aces.

Obviously, declarer doesn't know which black suit finesse to take and is trying to bait you into a cover. Being a great player, you, of course, have worked this all out and have ducked . . . smoothly.

Declarer, taken in by your nonchalance, will surely refuse the spade finesse and take the club finesse instead. Curtains.

KEY LESSON POINTERS

1. WHEN PARTNER LEADS A LOW SPOT CARD, (FOURTH BEST) THE RULE OF 11 CAN BE VERY HELPFUL.
2. WATCH PARTNER'S COUNT SIGNALS. IT MAKES IT EASIER TO COUNT DECLARER'S TRICKS.
3. IF YOU KNOW THAT DECLARER NEEDS ONE OF TWO FINESSES TO MAKE HIS CONTRACT, STEER HIM OFF THE WINNING FINESSE AS YOU DID HERE.

(26) FOUR CARD SUIT OVERCALL

Neither side vulnerable
Dealer North

North
♠ Q 10 9
♡ 7 3 2
◇ A K J 7
♣ J 3 2

West (you)
♠ A 7 6
♡ A K Q J
◇ 4 3
♣ 10 7 6 5

North	East	South	West
Pass	Pass	1 ◇	1 ♡
3 ◇	Pass	3 ♠	Pass
4 ♠	All Pass		

Opening lead: ♡ Q (asking for count)

Partner plays high-low in hearts and you continue with a third round which declarer ruffs with the ♠2. At trick four declarer leads the ♠K.

1. Do you take this trick? If so, what do you return?
2. You duck the trick and declarer continues with the ♠8. Do you take this trick? If so, what do you return?
3. What is your general plan?

FOUR CARD SUIT OVERCALL (Solution)

North
♠ Q 10 9
♡ 7 3 2
◇ A K J 7
♣ J 3 2

West
♠ A 7 6
♡ A K Q J
◇ 4 3
♣ 10 7 6 5

East
♠ 5 4 3
♡ 9 8 5 4
◇ 6 5
♣ Q 9 8 4

South
♠ K J 8 2
♡ 10 6
◇ Q 10 9 6 2
♣ A K

Duck both spades. The reason is that declarer is surely playing a 4-3 spade fit and has already been tapped down to your size. If you duck two rounds of spades, what can declarer do?

If he plays a third spade, death. You win and cash your heart. If he plays on diamonds, partner ruffs the third round and your spade ace defeats the contract one trick.

Had you won either the first or the second spade you would have no way of getting another trick. If you return a spade, declarer claims; if you return a heart, declarer ruffs in dummy, crosses to his hand with a club and draws the remaining trumps and claims.

It doesn't even matter if your partner has the dreaded ♠ Jxx. As long as you duck two rounds of spades, declarer is helpless.

KEY LESSON POINTERS

1. WHEN DECLARER IS PLAYING A 4-3 TRUMP FIT AND THE FOUR CARD HOLDING HAS BEEN SHORTENED, IT IS OFTEN BEST DEFENSE FOR THE PLAYER WITH Axx IN THE TRUMP SUIT TO DUCK TWICE.
2. THE DEFENSE AGAINST A 4-3 TRUMP FIT IS A WHOLE NEW BALL GAME. WHEN YOU ARE REASONABLY SURE THAT THEY ARE INVOLVED IN A 4-3 FIT, THE PLAY IS APT TO BE STICKY FOR THE DECLARER IF: (1) THE FOUR CARD HOLDING IS FORCED; (2) ONE OF THE DEFENDERS HAS FOUR TRUMPS.

(27) PERCEPTION

Neither side vulnerable
Dealer North

North
♠ 4
♡ Q J 10 9 6
◇ A Q 10 9 6
♣ 7 4

East (you)
♠ 7 3
♡ A 8 5 2
◇ 8 4 3 2
♣ A 10 3

North	East	South	West
Pass	Pass	1 ♠	Pass
2 ♡	Pass	3 ♠	Pass
4 ◇	Pass	4 ♠	All Pass

Opening lead: ♣ Q

1. Do you win this trick, if so, what do you return at trick two?

PERCEPTION   (Solution)

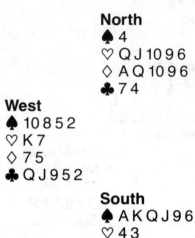

North
- ♠ 4
- ♡ Q J 10 9 6
- ◇ A Q 10 9 6
- ♣ 7 4

West
- ♠ 10 8 5 2
- ♡ K 7
- ◇ 7 5
- ♣ Q J 9 5 2

East
- ♠ 7 3
- ♡ A 8 5 2
- ◇ 8 4 3 2
- ♣ A 10 3

South
- ♠ A K Q J 9 6
- ♡ 4 3
- ◇ K J
- ♣ K 8 6

Win this trick. The threat of the diamond suit along with the apparent strength of South's spade suit indicates that you should start cashing your tricks immediately!

Your best chance by far is to hope partner has the doubleton ♡ K plus a promotable spade trick. Your play at trick two should be a low heart. Partner wins and returns a heart. Your third round of hearts promotes partner's ten of spades to the setting trick.

KEY LESSON POINTERS

1. WHEN THE DUMMY COMES DOWN WITH A STRONG SIDE SUIT AND DECLARER'S BIDDING HAS INDICATED A STRONG TRUMP SUIT, IT IS IMPERATIVE THAT THE DEFENDERS "GET BUSY" AND CASH THEIR WINNERS AT ONCE.
2. BEFORE MAKING A PLAY TO TRICK ONE, CONSIDER THE BIDDING, THE DUMMY IN RELATIONSHIP TO YOUR HAND, THE OPENING LEAD, AND FINALLY WHAT YOU NEED TO FIND IN PARTNER'S HAND TO DEFEAT THE CONTRACT. OF COURSE, IF YOU CAN DO ALL OF THAT, WHY ARE YOU READING THIS BOOK?

(28)   TEN, TEN, WHO'S GOT THE TEN?

East-West vulnerable
Dealer West

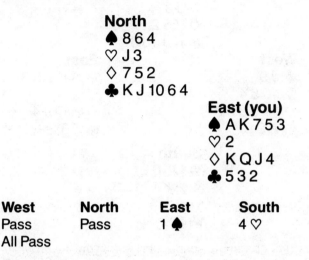

North
♠ 8 6 4
♡ J 3
◇ 7 5 2
♣ K J 10 6 4

East (you)
♠ A K 7 5 3
♡ 2
◇ K Q J 4
♣ 5 3 2

West	North	East	South
Pass	Pass	1 ♠	4 ♡
All Pass			

Opening lead: ♠ J

1. You win the ♠ K, declarer playing the ♠ 2. What do you play to trick two?
2. You play the ♠ A and declarer follows with the ♠ Q and partner the ♠ 9. What do you play to trick three?

TEN, TEN, WHO'S GOT THE TEN?   (Solution)

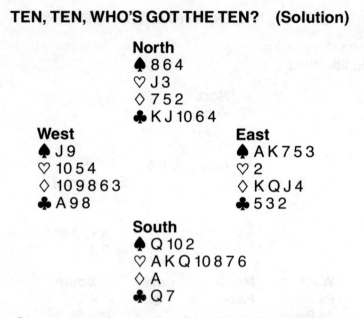

North
♠ 8 6 4
♡ J 3
◊ 7 5 2
♣ K J 10 6 4

West
♠ J 9
♡ 10 5 4
◊ 10 9 8 6 3
♣ A 9 8

East
♠ A K 7 5 3
♡ 2
◊ K Q J 4
♣ 5 3 2

South
♠ Q 10 2
♡ A K Q 10 8 7 6
◊ A
♣ Q 7

Give your partner a spade ruff, leading the seven while you're at it to ask for a diamond return.

The missing spade is the ten. If partner started with ♠ J 10 9, his proper second play would be the ♠ 10. Once he played the ♠9, he denied the ♠ 10. Knowing that, your play is clear. Partner's ace of clubs becomes the setting trick.

KEY LESSON POINTERS

1. WHEN LEADING THE TOP OF A THREE CARD SEQUENCE, FOLLOW DOWN THE LINE. HOWEVER, WHEN *MARKED* WITH THE MIDDLE HONOR, PLAY THE LOWEST:

    North
    ♠ K 4 2

    West
    ♠ Q J 10

    East
    ♠ A 9 8 7 6

    South
    ♠ 5 4

    YOU LEAD THE ♠ Q WHICH HOLDS THE TRICK. PARTNER KNOWS YOU HAVE THE ♠ J (OR ELSE DECLARER WOULD HAVE COVERED) SO CONTINUE WITH THE ♠ 10. IF YOU CONTINUE WITH THE ♠ J, YOU ARE DENYING THE ♠ 10!

2. WHEN LEADING THE TOP OF THREE *SMALL* CARDS, ALSO PLAY THE MIDDLE ONE NEXT. PLAYING THE LOWEST INDICATES A DOUBLETON.

(29) READING THE POSITION

Both sides vulnerable
Dealer South

North
♠ A K J 5
♡ 9 6
◇ 10 9 7
♣ 10 6 5 4

East (you)
♠ Q 10 3
♡ 10 8 3 2
◇ A Q 3
♣ Q 9 3

South	West	North	East
1 NT	Pass	2 ♣	Pass
2 ◇	Pass	2 NT	Pass
3 NT	All Pass		

Opening Lead: ♡ 4

Dummy plays the ♡ 9 and your ♡ 10 is taken with the ♡ K. Declarer cashes the ♣ A, crosses to the ♠ K, partner playing the ♠ 4, and leads a club to the jack, partner following.

A second spade is led to dummy's jack, partner playing the ♠ 8, (The ♠ 2 has not been seen) and you win the ♠ Q.

1. How many hearts does declarer have?
2. How many spades?
3. How many clubs?
4. How many high card points?
5. How many has he shown up with so far?
6. What do you lead at this point?
7. Assume you lead the ◇ A, declarer plays the ◇ 4 and partner the ◇ 6. How do you continue?

READING THE POSITION (Solution)

North
♠ A K J 5
♡ 9 6
◊ 10 9 7
♣ 10 6 5 4

West
♠ 9 8 4
♡ Q J 5 4
◊ K 6 5 2
♣ 7 2

East
♠ Q 10 3
♡ 10 8 3 2
◊ A Q 3
♣ Q 9 3

South
♠ 7 6 2
♡ A K 7
◊ J 8 4
♣ A K J 8

1. Three, partner has led his lowest heart so you know that he started with a four card suit.
2. Three. Partner played up the line.
3. Four. Regardless of how partner has played. If declarer had three clubs he would have cashed them at once so as not to be blocked out of his fourth club in dummy while he still had a spade entry.
4. 16 or 17. He accepted an invitational raise.
5. 11. The ♡ K, and the ♣ A K J. (Also a total of 8 tricks).

In order to defeat this contract you must find your partner with either the ♡ A Jxx or the ◊ Kxxx. In order to give yourself two chances, cash the ◊ A and see what partner plays.

His play of the ◊ 6 is a relatively high spot card (two lower ones are missing). Continue with the ◊ Q and collect four diamond tricks. You play so beautifully.

KEY LESSON POINTERS

1. REMEMBER THE EXACT SPOT CARD PARTNER HAS LED.
2. KEEP TRACK OF THE NUMBER OF HIGH CARD POINTS DECLARER HAS TURNED UP WITH.
3. IF YOU CAN GIVE YOURSELF TWO CHANCES TO DEFEAT A CONTRACT RATHER THAN ONE, GO FOR IT.

(30) WHAT DOES IT ALL MEAN?

North-South vulnerable
Dealer East

North
♠ A K J 9 8 5
♡ 5 3
◇ Q 8 7 4
♣ J

West (you)
♠ Q 10 6 3
♡ A
◇ K J 9 3 2
♣ 10 5 2

East	South	West	North
4 ♡	5 ♣	All Pass	

Opening lead: ♡A

Partner plays the ♡Q, declarer the ♡7.
1. What do you play at trick two?

WHAT DOES IT ALL MEAN?   (Solution)

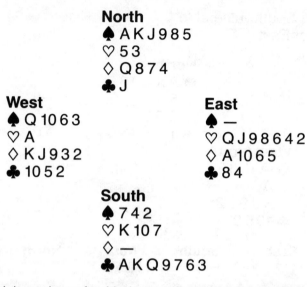

North
♠ A K J 9 8 5
♡ 5 3
◇ Q 8 7 4
♣ J

West
♠ Q 10 6 3
♡ A
◇ K J 9 3 2
♣ 10 5 2

East
♠ —
♡ Q J 9 8 6 4 2
◇ A 10 6 5
♣ 8 4

South
♠ 7 4 2
♡ K 10 7
◇ —
♣ A K Q 9 7 6 3

A high spade, preferably the ten. (Even the queen!) When partner has preempted and you lead an honor, partner can afford to give you a suit preference, rather than an attitude play, simply because he has so many cards from which to choose.

His play of the ♡Q definitely asks for a ♠ shift. As you are practically certain partner is going to ruff, give him a suit preference return signal. Your play of a high spade asks for a heart return. Had you returned a low spade, you would be asking for a diamond. Partner has to know which red suit to return in order to defeat this contract.

KEY LESSON POINTERS

1. WHEN THIRD HAND IS KNOWN TO HAVE A LONG SUIT FROM THE BIDDING (AT LEAST SIX CARDS) HIS FIRST PLAY CAN BE CONSIDERED SUIT PREFERENCE WHEN PARTNER LEADS A HIGH HONOR.
2. WHEN GIVING PARTNER A RUFF, TELL PARTNER WHICH SUIT YOU WANT RETURNED BY THE SIZE OF THE CARD YOU LEAD. A HIGH SPOT INDICATES A DESIRE FOR A SWITCH TO THE HIGHER RANKING SIDE SUIT, A LOW SPOT TO THE LOWER RANKING SIDE SUIT. SORRY, NO SIGNAL ASKS FOR A TRUMP RETURN. A NEUTRAL SPOT CARD RETURN ASKS PARTNER TO USE HIS JUDGEMENT—ALWAYS DANGEROUS.

(31)   KEEPING COOL

East-West vulnerable
Dealer South

North
♠ K 7 4 3
♡ Q J
◇ Q 5 4 2
♣ 8 7 4

West (you)
♠ A 8
♡ 10 8 7 5 3
◇ K J 8
♣ Q 3 2

South	West	North	East
1 ♣	Pass	1 ◇	Pass
1 ♠	Pass	2 ♠	All Pass

Opening lead: ♡ 5

Partner wins the ace and returns the ♡ 4, declarer playing the ♡ 2 and then the ♡ K.

1. At trick three declarer leads the ♠ J, which spade do you play, why?
2. You win the ace, what do you return?
3. After exiting with a spade, declarer wins with the ♠ Q, cashes the ♣ A, enters dummy with the ♠ K (you discard a heart), and leads a club to the jack and queen. On the clubs your partner has played low-high. What is declarer's distribution?
4. After you win your ♣ Q, what do you return?
5. You return a club to declarer's king, partner following with the ten. At this point declarer leads the ◇ 9, which diamond do you play?

KEEPING COOL   (Solution)

North
♠ K 7 4 3
♡ Q J
◇ Q 5 4 2
♣ 8 7 4

West
♠ A 8
♡ 10 8 7 5 3
◇ K J 8
♣ Q 3 2

East
♠ 9 5 2
♡ A 9 6 4
◇ A 7 6
♣ 10 9 5

South
♠ Q J 10 6
♡ K 2
◇ 10 9 3
♣ A K J 6

1. Rise with the ♠A, because you are in danger of being endplayed. Which suit are you going to break if you duck the first spade and win the second? Besides, if partner has the ♠Q, your play of the ♠A hasn't cost anything. Declarer has made a clever deceptive play in spades, but you were too smart, right?
2. Exit with a trump to avoid breaking a new suit.
3. Declarer is known to have four spades and two hearts. If partner is giving you a count signal in clubs, declarer has four clubs and, therefore, three diamonds.
4. Exit safely with a club and wait for declarer to break diamonds.
5. Cover with the ◇ J. Partner is marked with the ◇ A, (declarer has already turned up with 14 high card points) collect your three diamond tricks and defeat the contract.

KEY LESSON POINTERS

1. THERE IS A DANGER IN DUCKING ONE ROUND OF TRUMPS HOLDING Ax—IF YOU DON'T HAVE A SAFE EXIT. BETTER TO GRAB THE ACE AND EXIT WITH A TRUMP IF YOU WISH TO PLAY A PASSIVE DEFENSE.
2. KEEP TRACK OF DECLARER'S DISTRIBUTION FROM THE BIDDING AND PARTNER'S COUNT SIGNALS.
3. WHEN IT COMES DOWN TO THE NITTY-GRITTY AT THE END OF A HAND, IT PAYS TO KNOW WHO HAS WHICH MISSING HIGH HONORS. YOU WILL KNOW IF YOU KEEP TRACK OF THE POINTS DECLARER (AND/OR PARTNER) HAS TURNED UP WITH EARLIER IN THE PLAY.

(32) HE NEVER BID DIAMONDS

North-South vulnerable
Dealer West

North
♠ A K J 4
♡ —
◇ A K 8 7 4 3 2
♣ A K

East (you)
♠ Q 9 5 2
♡ 8
◇ Q J 10
♣ 8 7 6 3 2

West	North	East	South
3 ♡	4 ♡	Pass	6 ♣
All Pass			

Opening lead: 5 ◇

Dummy wins and the declarer follows. The ace and king of trumps are played, partner following once and then discarding the ♡ 7.

1. How do you play your trumps to show partner five? At trick four declarer cashes a high diamond, partner discarding the ♡ 6 and continues with a low diamond, partner discarding the ♠ 8 and declarer the ♡ 3.
2. What do you return at trick six?

HE NEVER BID DIAMONDS (Solution)

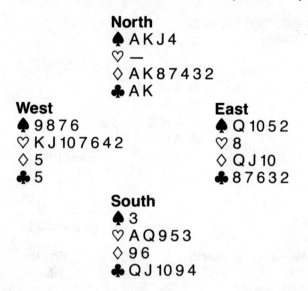

North
♠ A K J 4
♡ —
♢ A K 8 7 4 3 2
♣ A K

West
♠ 9 8 7 6
♡ K J 10 7 6 4 2
♢ 5
♣ 5

East
♠ Q 10 5 2
♡ 8
♢ Q J 10
♣ 8 7 6 3 2

South
♠ 3
♡ A Q 9 5 3
♢ 9 6
♣ Q J 10 9 4

1. High-low in trumps shows an odd number, the opposite of the count signal in the plain suits.
2. A spade. Any spade will do. Partner's discard of the ♠8 must be a count discard as he cannot have anything of value in the suit.

Partner must have either two or four spades. If he has two, along with his two known minor suit singletons he must be credited with nine hearts! Hardly. No, partner has four spades and seven hearts. As you have no assurance partner has the ♡A, you can insure a set by returning a spade. Let declarer discard two more hearts on the spades. In the end you ruff any diamond play and partner must make a heart trick if he has as little as the ♡K.

KEY LESSON POINTERS

1. A HIGH-LOW IN THE TRUMP SUIT SHOWS AN ODD NUMBER OF TRUMPS.
* 2. WHEN PARTNER IS PRESUMED TO BE MAKING A "COUNT" DIS-CARD, A HIGH SPOT CARD INDICATES AN EVEN NUMBER OF CARDS, A LOW SPOT CARD AN ODD NUMBER.
* In this book second highest is usually played with four cards to avoid any ambiguity with a doubleton. (If the highest missing spot card is played it is presumably from a doubleton). However, many good players routinely discard the highest from four small.
* Yes, declarer erred. He should have ruffed the ♢, cashed the two remaining trumps, the ♡A, and then entered dummy with a ♠ to run the ♢s. East ruffs but must return a ♠.

(33)   THE TENDER TRAP

Both sides vulnerable
Dealer East

North
♠ 2
♡ Q 4 2
◇ K 10 9 8
♣ K J 10 9 8

West (you)
♠ J 8 4 3
♡ J 7
◇ 6 5 3
♣ Q 7 4 2

East	South	West	North
2 ♡*	4 ♠	All Pass	

* Weak Two Bid
Opening lead: ♡ J

Dummy plays low and partner signals encouragement. You continue with a second heart to partner's king and partner continues with the ♡ A which declarer ruffs with the ♠ 10.
1. Do you overruff?
2. If you do, what do you return; if you don't, what do you discard?

THE TENDER TRAP   (Solution)

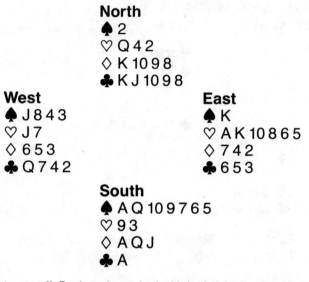

North
♠ 2
♡ Q 4 2
◇ K 10 9 8
♣ K J 10 9 8

West
♠ J 8 4 3
♡ J 7
◇ 6 5 3
♣ Q 7 4 2

East
♠ K
♡ A K 10 8 6 5
◇ 7 4 2
♣ 6 5 3

South
♠ A Q 10 9 7 6 5
♡ 9 3
◇ A Q J
♣ A

1. Do not overruff. Declarer is marked with both minor suit aces, so it is unlikely you have any minor suit tricks coming. But, partner might have either the king or queen of spades. If so, by not overtrumping you emerge with two trump tricks. Overtrump and you wind up with only one.
2. Your discard is immaterial, but a low diamond is reasonable.

KEY LESSON POINTERS

1. DO NOT OVERTRUMP IN BACK OF A STRONG TRUMP SUIT WITH THREE OR FOUR CARDS TO A HIGH HONOR. IF YOU HAVE AN INTERMEDIATE SPOT CARD AS WELL (AN EIGHT MAY BE ENOUGH), YOU WILL WIND UP WITH AN EXTRA TRUMP TRICK IF PARTNER HAS AN HONOR OR EVEN A HIGH SPOT CARD. CONSIDER THIS LAYOUT:

North
♠ 3

West
♠ Q 8 5 2

East
♠ 9 4

South
♠ A K J 10 7 6

EAST LEADS AN OFF SUIT THAT NEITHER SOUTH NOR WEST HAS. SOUTH RUFFS WITH THE ♠J. IF WEST OVERTRUMPS IT IS HIS LAST TRUMP TRICK, BUT IF WEST DISCARDS, HE COMES TO TWO TRUMP TRICKS.

SIMILARLY, IF WEST LEADS A SUIT THAT NEITHER EAST NOR SOUTH HAS, EAST RUFFS WITH THE ♠9 "UPPERCUTTING" SOUTH. SOUTH OVERTRUMPS BUT EVENTUALLY MUST LOSE TWO TRICKS TO WEST.

(34)　IT'S ON YOUR HEAD

East-West vulnerable
Dealer West

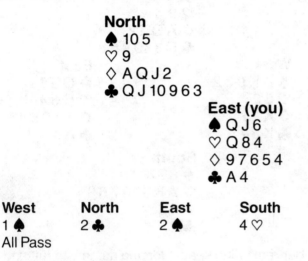

North
♠ 10 5
♡ 9
◊ A Q J 2
♣ Q J 10 9 6 3

East (you)
♠ Q J 6
♡ Q 8 4
◊ 9 7 6 5 4
♣ A 4

West	North	East	South
1 ♠	2 ♣	2 ♠	4 ♡
All Pass			

Opening lead: ♠ K

1. Which spade do you play?
2. You play the ♠ Q and partner returns the ♠ 3 to your ♠ J, declarer playing the ♠ 7 and ♠ 8. What do you play to trick three?
3. You try the ♣ A; partner plays the ♣ 8, and declarer, the ♣ 2. What do you play to trick four?

IT'S ON YOUR HEAD   (Solution)

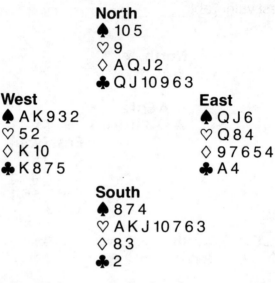

North
♠ 10 5
♡ 9
◇ A Q J 2
♣ Q J 10 9 6 3

West
♠ A K 9 3 2
♡ 5 2
◇ K 10
♣ K 8 7 5

East
♠ Q J 6
♡ Q 8 4
◇ 9 7 6 5 4
♣ A 4

South
♠ 8 7 4
♡ A K J 10 7 6 3
◇ 8 3
♣ 2

Your remaining spade, forcing dummy to ruff and establishing your ♡ Q as the setting trick.

When partner returns the ♠ 3, his original fourth best, you know that declarer has another spade as partner cannot have more than five spades. As declarer may not have another club, and the spade return gives you a sure set, there really is no choice.

KEY LESSON POINTERS

1. THE PLAY OF THE QUEEN UNDER PARTNER'S KING PROMISES THE JACK IF YOU HAVE SUPPORTED THE SUIT. IF YOU HAVE NOT, IT COULD ALSO BE A SINGLETON OR FROM Qx IF THE JACK IS IN THE DUMMY.
2. TRADITIONALLY, WHEN PARTNER UNDERLEADS AFTER HAVING LED AN HONOR, HIS SECOND CARD IS HIS ORIGINAL FOURTH BEST.*
3. ONE WAY OF SCORING AN OTHERWISE FINESSABLE TRUMP WINNER, IS TO MAKE SURE THAT YOUR TRUMP HONOR CANNOT BE FINESSED. FORCING THE DUMMY TO RUFF IS ONE WAY TO DO THIS.

* PRESENT COUNT IS BETTER.

(35)   WHEN?

East-West vulnerable
Dealer South

                        North
                        ♠ Q 4 3
                        ♡ Q 6 5
                        ◇ 7 6 3
                        ♣ A Q J 9
        West (you)
        ♠ A 5 4 2
        ♡ J 10
        ◇ A K J 8
        ♣ 8 6 5

South	**West**	**North**	**East**
1 ♠	Pass	2 ♣	Pass
2 ♡	Pass	2 ♠	Pass
4 ♠	All Pass		

Opening lead: ◇ K

1. Partner plays the ◇ 9, declarer the ◇ 2. What do you think partner has in diamonds?
2. What do you play at trick two? Why?
3. You continue with the ace and a diamond, declarer ruffing the third round. Declarer leads the ♠ K, do you take this trick? If so, what do you return? If not, what is your plan?

WHEN? (Solution)

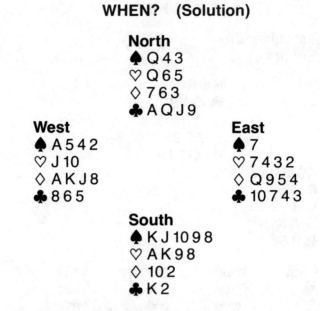

North
♠ Q 4 3
♡ Q 6 5
◊ 7 6 3
♣ A Q J 9

West
♠ A 5 4 2
♡ J 10
◊ A K J 8
♣ 8 6 5

East
♠ 7
♡ 7 4 3 2
◊ Q 9 5 4
♣ 10 7 4 3

South
♠ K J 10 9 8
♡ A K 9 8
◊ 10 2
♣ K 2

1. The ◊Q, more likely than a doubleton on the bidding.
2. The ◊A to try to shorten declarer to your trump length.
3. Duck the ♠K. In order to shorten declarer a second time you must win the trump that EXHAUSTS dummy. In other words, the third round of trumps. Now, when you play a fourth diamond, declarer must trump with his last trump. If declarer stops drawing trumps after two rounds, you ruff the third round of hearts. Down one.

KEY LESSON POINTERS

1. A HIGH-SPOT CARD SIGNAL IN RESPONSE TO THE LEAD OF AN HONOR IN AN UNSUPPORTED SUIT EITHER SHOWS A DOUBLETON OR AN EQUAL HONOR. USE THE BIDDING TO DETERMINE WHICH IS MORE LIKELY.
2. HOLDING FOUR TRUMPS IT IS USUALLY RIGHT TO LEAD YOUR LONGEST SUIT IN THE HOPES OF FORCING DE-CLARER TO RUFF.
3. WHEN BOTH DECLARER AND DUMMY ARE VOID OF THE SUIT THAT YOU WISH TO MAKE DECLARER TRUMP, WIN YOUR TRUMP TRICK AT THE SAME TIME DUMMY WILL BE EXHAUSTED IN TRUMPS. (IF DUMMY HAS TWO TRUMPS, WIN THE SECOND ROUND, IF DUMMY HAS THREE TRUMPS, WIN THE THIRD ROUND).

(36) SHORT SUIT LEADS

Both sides vulnerable
Dealer South

North
♠ 10 9 2
♡ 8 4 3
♦ A K Q 10 9
♣ Q 9

West (you)
♠ A 6
♡ 9 7 6 5 2
♦ J
♣ K 8 7 5 3

South	West	North	East
1 ♠	Pass	2 ♦	Pass
2 ♠	Pass	3 ♠	Pass
4 ♠	All Pass		

Opening lead: ♦ J

Dummy wins, partner playing the ♦ 2 and declarer the
♦ 4. At trick two the ♠ 10 is led from dummy, partner plays the
♠ 3 and declarer the ♠ 7, and you win.
1. What do you return, and why?

SHORT SUIT LEADS   (Solution)

North
♠ 10 9 2
♡ 8 4 3
◇ A K Q 10 9
♣ Q 9

West
♠ A 6
♡ 9 7 6 5 2
◇ J
♣ K 8 7 5 3

East
♠ 5 4 3
♡ Q J 10
◇ 8 7 3 2
♣ A 6 4

South
♠ K Q J 8 7
♡ A K
◇ 6 5 4
♣ J 10 2

The ♣ K! Partner presumably recognizes your lead as a singleton (it is rare to lead dummy's first bid suit with a doubleton honor), and his duty at trick one is to indicate where his outside strength lies. His ◇ 2 clearly indicates the ♣ A.

Leading the ♣ K and then a club prevents partner from making a mistake. If you lead a low club, partner might decide to return the suit or, perhaps, shift to a heart, fearing you led from a doubleton diamond. No reason to take an unnecessary chance. (Give yourself full credit if you switched to a club).

KEY LESSON POINTERS

1. WHEN AN OVBIOUS SINGLETON IS LED, THIRD HAND GIVES SUIT PREFERENCE, NOT ATTITUDE OR COUNT.
2. ANTICIPATING PARTNER'S PROBLEMS IS THE HALLMARK OF A GREAT DEFENDER. MAKING LIFE EASIER FOR PARTNER SHOULD BE YOUR GOAL—NO MATTER WHAT HE DID TO YOU ON THE LAST HAND—.

(37)   PUSHING THEM AROUND

Neither side vulnerable
Dealer West

North
♠ 6 2
♡ A Q 2
◇ J 10 8 7 4 2
♣ K Q

East (you)
♠ 3
♡ J 10 8 7 6
◇ A 5
♣ J 7 6 5 3

West	North	East	South
3 ♠	Pass	Pass	3 NT
Pass	4 NT	All Pass	

Opening lead: ♠ K

The ♠K holds, declarer playing the ♠9. At trick two partner continues with the ♠Q. What do you discard?

PUSHING THEM AROUND   (Solution)

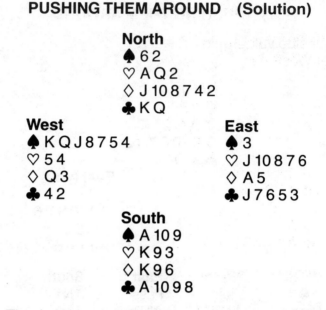

North
♠ 6 2
♡ A Q 2
◇ J 10 8 7 4 2
♣ K Q

West
♠ K Q J 8 7 5 4
♡ 5 4
◇ Q 3
♣ 4 2

East
♠ 3
♡ J 10 8 7 6
◇ A 5
♣ J 7 6 5 3

South
♠ A 10 9
♡ K 9 3
◇ K 9 6
♣ A 10 9 8

The ◇ A! In order to defeat this contract partner needs a side entry. It can't be in hearts, so it has to be in either diamonds or clubs.

Partner's play of the ♠Q (instead of the ♠J) indicates that his entry is in the higher ranking of the two possible suits. If partner's lone face card is the doubleton ◇Q you have to discard the ◇A to make sure partner gets the lead.

If you discard anything else, declarer must play you for the ◇A as the hand cannot be made if partner has it. In fact, if you discard anything else, declarer makes an overtrick.

KEY LESSON POINTERS

1. WHEN PARTNER HAS EQUAL HONORS HE CAN USE THEM TO INDICATE WHERE HIS SIDE STRENGTH LIES.
2. Ax OR Kx IN BACK OF A LONG WEAK SUIT CAN BE AN IMPEDIMENT IF PARTNER HAS Qx IN THE SAME SUIT. IN THAT CASE THE HIGH HONOR MUST BE UN-BLOCKED EARLY TO CREATE AN ENTRY INTO PART-NER'S HAND.

(38) FOUR JACKS SHOWING

Neither side vulnerable
Dealer North

> **North**
> ♠ A 4
> ♡ A K 4
> ◇ K Q J 10 8 7
> ♣ Q J

West (you)
♠ J 9 8 6 2
♡ J 10 9
◇ A
♣ A 10 8 3

North	East	South	West
1 ◇	Pass	1 NT	Pass
3 NT	All Pass		

Opening lead: ♠ 6

1. Dummy plays the ♠A, partner the ♠5, and declarer the ♠Q. How do you read this suit?
2. The ◇K is led from dummy, partner plays the deuce and declarer the three. After making the thoughtful play of taking the trick, how do you continue?

FOUR JACKS SHOWING   (Solution)

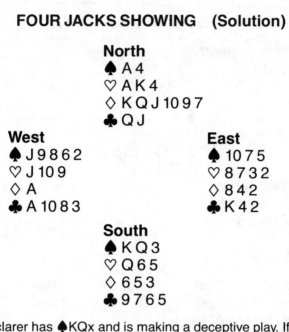

North
♠ A 4
♡ A K 4
♢ K Q J 10 9 7
♣ Q J

West
♠ J 9 8 6 2
♡ J 10 9
♢ A
♣ A 10 8 3

East
♠ 10 7 5
♡ 8 7 3 2
♢ 8 4 2
♣ K 4 2

South
♠ K Q 3
♡ Q 6 5
♢ 6 5 3
♣ 9 7 6 5

1. Declarer has ♠KQx and is making a deceptive play. If declarer had ♠KQ partner would have ♠10753. With that holding he should play low at trick one, reserving his come-on signals to show either the Q or K when dummy wins the first trick with an unsupported ace.

2. Shift to the ♣A! Declarer has nine tricks in sight outside of clubs (two spades, five diamonds and at least two hearts), so you need four club tricks.

   There are two possibilities. Partner has specifically ♣K9 doubleton in which case you must shift to a low club, or partner has ♣Kxx in which case you must shift to the ace, then the ♣2 to partner's ♣K and wait for partner to return a third club through declarer's guarded ♣9.

   The second possibility is more likely.

KEY LESSON POINTERS

1. WHEN DUMMY WINS A SPOT CARD OPENING LEAD WITH AN UNSUPPORTED ACE, THIRD HAND SIGNALS ENCOURAGEMENT WITH THE Q OR K, OTHERWISE, LOW.
2. KEEP A RUNNING COUNT OF DECLARER'S TRICKS.
3. WHEN PARTNER MUST HAVE ONE OF TWO HOLDINGS TO DEFEAT A CONTRACT, PLAY FOR THE ONE THAT IS MORE PROBABLE.

(39) JAWS

East-West vulnerable
Dealer North

North
♠ Q J 7 6 2
♡ A J 10
◇ J
♣ J 10 6 5

East (you)
♠ 8 3
♡ K 8 6 4
◇ 9 8 5 4 3
♣ A 2

North	East	South	West
Pass	Pass	1 ♣	Pass
1 ♠	Pass	1 NT	Pass
3 ♣	Pass	5 ♣	All Pass

Opening lead: ◇ K

1. Which diamond do you play?
2. Declarer wins and plays the ♣Q which you win, partner playing the ♣3. How many clubs do you think declarer has?
3. What do you return at trick three, and why?

JAWS   (Solution)

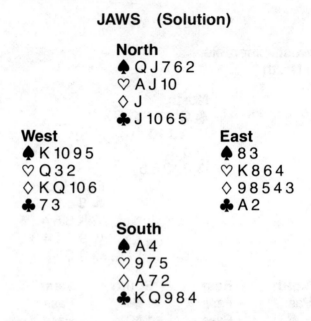

North
♠ Q J 7 6 2
♡ A J 10
◇ J
♣ J 10 6 5

West
♠ K 10 9 5
♡ Q 3 2
◇ K Q 10 6
♣ 7 3

East
♠ 8 3
♡ K 8 6 4
◇ 9 8 5 4 3
♣ A 2

South
♠ A 4
♡ 9 7 5
◇ A 7 2
♣ K Q 9 8 4

1. ◇ 3. No reason to play anything else. You want a heart shift, so play a low diamond to make sure partner doesn't think you like diamonds.
2. Almost certainly five. With six, South would have rebid the suit and with four might have done some further notrump investigation. Furthermore, if declarer has four clubs, partner has three, and partner usually gives count in the trump suit by playing the middle of three trumps. Partner played his lowest trump.
3. A low heart. Count tricks. If declarer has five clubs he can take at least *six* club tricks (four in his hand plus two ◇ ruffs in dummy). He must have at least one spade honor which means he can set up that suit for at least three tricks. Those three spades along with six trumps and two red aces make eleven tricks. An active defense is called for. Return a heart hoping partner has the ♡ Q along with a spade honor.

KEY LESSON POINTERS

1. TRY TO TAKE A READING ON THE NUMBER OF TRUMPS DE-CLARER HAS FROM THE BIDDING.
2. PARTNER USUALLY PLAYS HIGH-LOW IN THE TRUMP SUIT TO SHOW THREE OR FIVE. (DON'T HOLD YOUR BREATH WAITING FOR FIVE). LOW-HIGH INDICATES TWO OR FOUR TRUMPS.
3. COUNT DECLARER'S TRICKS INCLUDING DUMMY RUFFS. IF AN ATTACKING LEAD HAS TO BE MADE BEFORE THE LONG SUIT BE-COMES ESTABLISHED, MAKE IT.

(40)   BEAT THE SLAM

Both sides vulnerable
Dealer South

> **North**
> ♠ 2
> ♡ Q J 10
> ◊ 7 6 5
> ♣ A J 10 9 8 7

> **East (you)**
> ♠ 5 4 3
> ♡ K 9 8 7
> ◊ A 8 4
> ♣ Q 6 3

South	West	North	East
2 ♣*	Pass	3 ♣	Pass
3 ♠	Pass	4 ♣	Pass
4 NT	Pass	5 ◊	Pass
6 ♠	All Pass		

*Strong and artificial
Opening lead: ◊Q

1. Which diamond do you play at trick one?
2. You play the ◊A and declarer the ◊9. What do you return at trick two, why?

BEAT THE SLAM   (Solution)

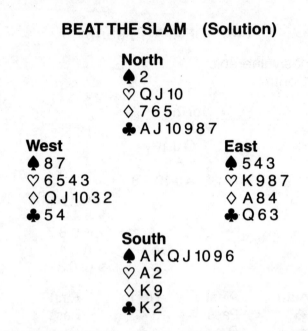

North
♠ 2
♡ Q J 10
♢ 7 6 5
♣ A J 10 9 8 7

West
♠ 8 7
♡ 6 5 4 3
♢ Q J 10 3 2
♣ 5 4

East
♠ 5 4 3
♡ K 9 8 7
♢ A 8 4
♣ Q 6 3

South
♠ A K Q J 10 9 6
♡ A 2
♢ K 9
♣ K 2

Any low heart. Before making your play to trick two, you should give some thought to declarer's hand. Remember, he does have a strong two spade opening.

Surely he has the ♢ K, the ♡ A, solid spades and the ♣ K. So what chance do you have knowing, as you do, that the heart finesse works?

Well, you know the heart finesse works, but the declarer doesn't. If declarer has the hand you see, his best chance for the contract is to test the clubs by playing the A K and if the queen does not drop, take the heart finesse. What if you play a heart at once?

Declarer will not have time to test the clubs and won't know which play to take. You have put declarer to the test early. Bravo. If declarer rises with the ace of hearts (he probably will), he can no longer make the hand. If you woodenly return a diamond, declarer makes the hand easily by drawing trumps, testing clubs, and later taking the ♡ finesse.

KEY LESSON POINTERS

1. TRY TO VISUALIZE DECLARER'S HAND FROM THE BIDDING.
2. IF YOU CAN SEE THAT DECLARER HAS A CHOICE OF PLAYS FOR HIS CONTRACT, WHICH INCLUDES TESTING A LONG SUIT BEFORE RELYING UPON A FINESSE, REMOVE THE OPTION BY LEADING THE FINESSE SUIT BEFORE THE LONG SUIT HAS BEEN TESTED.

(41) SEVEN TRUMPS IN DUMMY

East-West vulnerable
Dealer West

North
♠ A 5 2
♡ 4
◇ J 10 7 6 4 3 2
♣ 8 7

West (you)
♠ 10 8 7 6
♡ K 6 3
◇ —
♣ K Q J 10 5 3

West	North	East	South
Pass	Pass	Pass	1 ◇
2 ♣	4 ◇	5 ♣	5 ◇
Pass	Pass	Dbl.	All Pass

Opening lead: ♣ K

Partner plays the ♣ 6 and declarer the ♣ A.

1. How do you read the club suit?
2. Declarer leads the ◇8 to dummy's ◇10, partner following with the ◇5. Assuming you wish to give partner count in clubs, which club do you discard?
3. At trick three the ♡4 is led from dummy, partner plays the ♡2, declarer the ♡Q, and you win. What do you play to trick four?

SEVEN TRUMPS IN DUMMY (Solution)

North
♠ A 5 2
♡ 4
♦ J 10 7 6 4 3 2
♣ 8 7

West
♠ 10 8 7 6
♡ K 6 3
♦ —
♣ K Q J 10 5 3

East
♠ K Q 3
♡ A 9 8 7 2
♦ 5
♣ 9 6 4 2

South
♠ J 9 4
♡ Q J 10 5
♦ A K Q 9 8
♣ A

1. Partner should be giving count by playing second highest. He is allowed to do this because he has supported your suit.
2. The ♣ 3. Present count. You have an odd number of clubs remaining, so discard your lowest club.
3. A spade. Partner presumably has the ♡ A. If declarer has ♡ Q J 10x and you don't return a spade, declarer will ruff your club return, and lead the ♡J discarding a spade from the table. The other spade will go off on the ♡10. Partner needs the ♠ K Q to defeat this hand—so play for it. Partner wins your spade return and exits with a club. Declarer must lose another trick.

KEY LESSON POINTERS

1. IN A SUIT THAT HAS BEEN SUPPORTED, PARTNER USU-ALLY GIVES COUNT AT TRICK ONE WHEN THE KING IS LED. IF IT HASN'T BEEN SUPPORTED, ATTITUDE. (USUALLY.)
2. AFTER AN HONOR HAS BEEN LED, THE FIRST DISCARD IN THAT SUIT IS USUALLY PRESENT COUNT.
3. NOTICE HOW IMPORTANT IT IS FOR PARTNER TO DUCK THE HEART ACE EVEN THOUGH A SINGLETON IS LED. IF PARTNER GOES UP, DECLARER CAN TRUMP FINESSE YOUR ♡ K. DECLARER THEN MAKES AN OVERTRICK!

(42) THE CLUES ARE THERE, WATSON

East-West vulnerable
Dealer South

North
♠ Q 7 5
♡ Q 9
◇ K 8 5 4 3
♣ A J 6

West (you)
♠ A 9 4 3
♡ 4 3
◇ 10 9 2
♣ 9 5 3 2

South	West	North	East
1 ♣	Pass	1 ◇	4 ♡
4 ♠	Pass	5 ♣	All Pass

Opening lead: ♡ 4

Partner wins with the ♡K, declarer playing the ♡J. At trick two partner shifts to the ♠J, declarer plays low. Which spade do you play, why?

THE CLUES ARE THERE, WATSON   (Solution)

North
♠ Q 7 5
♡ Q 9
◇ K 8 5 4 3
♣ A J 6

West
♠ A 9 4 3
♡ 4 3
◇ 10 9 2
♣ 9 5 3 2

East
♠ J 10
♡ A K 10 8 7 6 5 2
◇ J 7 6
♣ —

South
♠ K 8 6 2
♡ J
◇ A Q
♣ K Q 10 8 7 4

The ♠4. Partner does not have a singleton spade. Had he a singleton spade, partner would have won the first trick with the ♡A, purposely concealing the ♡K, thus making it easier for you to play spades rather than hearts.

By ducking the first spade, declarer must lose two more tricks against best defense. Of course, best defense requires partner to unblock the ♠10 on an early trump play. Not to worry, your partner makes those plays routinely.

KEY LESSON POINTERS

1. THIRD HAND HAS A CERTAIN RESPONSIBILITY WHEN HOLDING THE A K IN THE SUIT PARTNER HAS LED. IF THIRD HAND IS INTENDING TO SHIFT TO A SHORT SUIT AT TRICK TWO, HE WINS WITH THE ACE IF HE IS SHIFTING TO A SINGLETON AND WITH THE KING IF HE IS SHIFTING TO A DOUBLETON. THEREFORE WHEN THIRD HAND WINS THE OPENING LEAD WITH THE KING AND SHIFTS TO A SHORT SUIT IT MUST BE A DOUBLETON. GOT IT?

(43) CONVENTIONS, CONVENTIONS

Both sides vulnerable
Dealer South

North
♠ A 7 4 3
♡ A Q J
♦ K J 10
♣ 7 4 2

East (you)
♠ K J
♡ 10 8 7
♦ A 9 7 5 3 2
♣ 10 8

South	West	North	East
1 ♠	Pass	3 NT*	Pass
4 ♠	All Pass		

*Balanced, forcing spade raise
Opening lead: ♦ 8

Dummy plays the ten, plan your defense.

CONVENTIONS, CONVENTIONS   (Solution)

North
♠ A 7 4 3
♡ A Q J
◇ K J 10
♣ 7 4 2

West
♠ 5 2
♡ 9 6 5 3 2
◇ 8
♣ K 9 6 5 3

East
♠ K J
♡ 10 8 7
◇ A 9 7 5 3 2
♣ 10 8

South
♠ Q 10 9 8 6
♡ K 4
◇ Q 6 4
♣ A Q J

The best chance to defeat this contract is to hope partner has a singleton diamond plus a club trick. (If you took the ace of diamonds and shifted to a club hoping partner had something like the ♣ A Q, you weren't being realistic.) Between you and dummy you can see 23 high card points. Giving declarer as little as 12, partner can have no more than 5 high card points and is unlikely to hold that many. Besides, club tricks aren't running away.

No, your play is to win the diamond and try to give partner a diamond ruff. But, be careful about which diamond you return. Remember, partner doesn't know you have a trump trick and is searching for another entry to your hand.

As a club shift from partner is likely to be disastrous and a heart shift can't hurt (no signal for a trump switch, sorry), return the ◇ 9 asking partner to return a heart, the safe suit. This defense defeats the contract one trick.

KEY LESSON POINTERS

1. ADD YOUR POINTS TO DUMMY'S THEN GIVE DECLARER SOME AVERAGE POINT COUNT TO DETERMINE HOW STRONG PARTNER IS.
2. WHEN GIVING PARTNER A RUFF, AND NOT HAVING ANY STRENGTH IN EITHER SIDE SUIT, ASK PARTNER TO RETURN THE SUIT THAT CAN'T HURT YOUR SIDE. THIS IS AN IMPORTANT DEFENSIVE CONCEPT.

(44)　SURE IS BEST

North-South vulnerable
Dealer North

North
♠ K 10 7 6
♡ 10
◇ Q 4
♣ A K Q 10 7 6

West (you)
♠ J 8 5 3
♡ A 9 3 2
◇ K 5
♣ J 9 2

North	East	South	West
1 ♣	2 ◇ *	2 ♡	3 ◇
Pass	Pass	3 ♡	Pass
3 ♠	Pass	4 ♡	All Pass

*Weak
Opening lead: ◇K

Partner plays the ◇7 and declarer the ◇3. What do you play to trick two?

SURE IS BEST   (Solution)

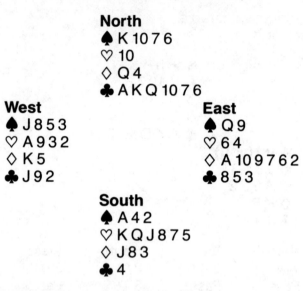

North
♠ K 10 7 6
♡ 10
♢ Q 4
♣ A K Q 10 7 6

West
♠ J 8 5 3
♡ A 9 3 2
♢ K 5
♣ J 9 2

East
♠ Q 9
♡ 6 4
♢ A 10 9 7 6 2
♣ 8 5 3

South
♠ A 4 2
♡ K Q J 8 7 5
♢ J 8 3
♣ 4

The ♡A. Then continue with a diamond to partner's ace. Partner plays a third diamond. If declarer has the jack, you ruff it for the setting trick. If partner has the ◇J it cashes, and then he plays a fourth diamond promoting your ♡9 for a two trick set. Even if partner has seven diamonds your play wins. When partner plays a third diamond your ♡9 promotes to the setting trick.

KEY LESSON POINTERS

1. TRY TO LOOK A TRICK OR TWO AHEAD. FOR EXAMPLE, ON THIS HAND IF YOU WOODENLY PLAY A SECOND DIAMOND AT TRICK TWO, YOU NO LONGER CAN DEFEAT THE CONTRACT IF DECLARER HAS THE ◇ J.
2. A WEAK JUMP OVERCALL AT THE TWO LEVEL GENERALLY SHOWS A SIX CARD SUIT. THE STRENGTH OF BOTH THE HAND AND THE SUIT TEXTURE VARIES WITH THE VULNERABILITY. CERTAIN RISKS SHOULD BE TAKEN AT FAVORABLE VULNERABILITY TO MUDDY THE WATERS—PARTICULARLY IF PARTNER IS A PASSED HAND.

(45) FOUR LEVEL PREEMPT

Both sides vulnerable
Dealer South

North
♠ 4 3 2
♡ A 9
♢ K Q 10 8
♣ A Q 4 2

East (you)
♠ Q 8 5
♡ K 5
♢ 7 4 2
♣ 10 8 7 6 5

South	West	North	East
1 ♢	4 ♡	5 ♢	All Pass

Opening lead: ♡ Q

Declarer wins in dummy, draws three rounds of trumps ending in dummy, partner discarding two hearts, and ruffs a heart in the closed hand.

Declarer continues by cashing the ♣ K, ♣ J, and leading a low club to dummy's ♣ Q. On the ♣ A declarer discards a low spade. Partner discards three hearts on the clubs.

At trick ten a low spade is led from dummy.

1. What was declarer's original distribution?
2. Which spade do you play, why?

FOUR LEVEL PREEMPT (Solution)

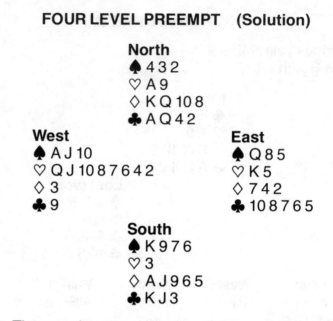

North
♠ 4 3 2
♡ A 9
♢ K Q 10 8
♣ A Q 4 2

West
♠ A J 10
♡ Q J 10 8 7 6 4 2
♢ 3
♣ 9

East
♠ Q 8 5
♡ K 5
♢ 7 4 2
♣ 10 8 7 6 5

South
♠ K 9 7 6
♡ 3
♢ A J 9 6 5
♣ K J 3

The count in every suit is clear. Declarer started with 4-1-5-3 distribution. He has stripped the hand and the defense needs three spade tricks to defeat the contract. From your point of view the only spade holding in partner's hand that will defeat the contract is the A J 10. If partner has that holding, you must play the ♠ Q to prevent declarer from ducking the trick into your partner.

KEY LESSON POINTERS

1. COUNT EVERY HAND AS IF YOUR LIFE DEPENDED UPON IT. GET IN THE HABIT. IT GETS EASIER AFTER A WHILE. (LIKE IN ABOUT 10 YEARS.)
2. KNOW HOW MANY TRICKS YOU NEED AT ANY GIVEN MOMENT TO DEFEAT THE CONTRACT.
3. WHEN A HAND HAS BEEN TOTALLY STRIPPED, AND DECLARER GETS AROUND TO THE LAST SUIT, YOU SHOULD KNOW DECLARER'S DISTRIBUTION AND HOW MANY TRICKS YOU NEED FROM THIS SUIT.
4. IN A STRIP AND END PLAY SITUATION, SECOND HAND FREQUENTLY MUST PLAY HIGH TO PREVENT PARTNER FROM GETTING ENDPLAYED.

(46)   YOU'RE IN!

Neither side vulnerable
Dealer West

North
♠ Q 9 8
♡ 4 3
◇ K 5 2
♣ A J 10 6 5

East (you)
♠ 10 6
♡ K J
◇ Q 10 4 3
♣ Q 9 8 3 2

West	North	East	South
4 ♡	Pass	Pass	4 ♠
All Pass			

Opening lead: ♡2

1. Which heart do you play?
2. You play the ♡K and it holds, what do you return at trick two? Why?

YOU'RE IN! (Solution)

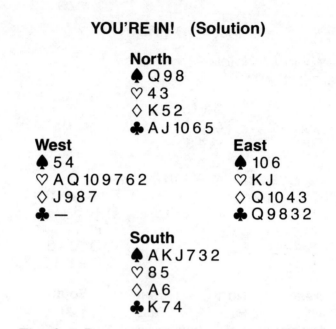

North
♠ Q 9 8
♡ 4 3
♦ K 5 2
♣ A J 10 6 5

West
♠ 5 4
♡ A Q 10 9 7 6 2
♦ J 9 8 7
♣ —

East
♠ 10 6
♡ K J
♦ Q 10 4 3
♣ Q 9 8 3 2

South
♠ A K J 7 3 2
♡ 8 5
♦ A 6
♣ K 7 4

The ♣ 9. Partner has made an unusual lead to alert you to a side void. As the void is clearly in clubs, return a high club to indicate that you have a possible reentry in the heart suit.

Your previous play of the ♡K has denied the ♡Q so partner will either play you for a void or the jack. If he has the ♡ AQ it is safe to underlead. If partner has the ♡A and no ♡Q he will play the ♡A. As you routinely trump partner's aces, you will trump if you are void and give partner another club ruff. Do your partners appreciate how well you really play?

KEY LESSON POINTERS

1. WHEN THE OPENING LEADER HAS A KNOWN LONG SUIT AND MAKES WHAT CANNOT BE AN "HONEST" LEAD, BE ON THE LOOKOUT FOR A SIDE VOID.
2. WHEN GIVING PARTNER A RUFF, DON'T GET SO EXCITED THAT YOU FORGET THAT YOUR RETURN IS ALSO A SIGNAL, A SUIT PREFERENCE SIGNAL.

(47)   LIMIT RAISE

North-South vulnerable
Dealer South

> **North**
> ♠ K 7 5 2
> ♡ 9 6 2
> ◇ K Q
> ♣ Q J 10 8

West (you)
♠ 10 8 3
♡ K Q 10 4 3
◇ 7 5 2
♣ 9 5

South	West	North	East
1 ♠	Pass	3 ♠	Pass
4 ♠	All Pass		

Opening lead: ♡ K

1. Partner ovetakes and returns the ♡ J. Which heart do you play?
2. You overtake and cash the ♡ 10 upon which partner discards the ♣ 2. What do you play to trick four?

LIMIT RAISE   (Solution)

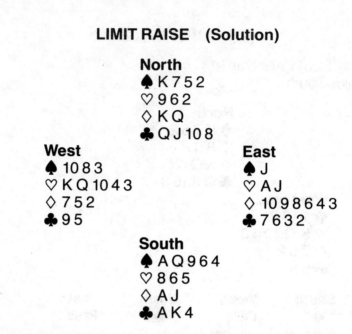

North
♠ K 7 5 2
♡ 9 6 2
♢ K Q
♣ Q J 10 8

West
♠ 10 8 3
♡ K Q 10 4 3
♢ 7 5 2
♣ 9 5

East
♠ J
♡ A J
♢ 10 9 8 6 4 3
♣ 7 6 3 2

South
♠ A Q 9 6 4
♡ 8 6 5
♢ A J
♣ A K 4

A fourth heart. Partner has nothing in clubs and did not cash the ♢A so he doesn't have anything in that suit either. Your only chance is to hope partner has a singleton honor in spades, which will promote your spade holding to the setting trick.

KEY LESSON POINTERS

1. USE PARTNER'S ATTITUDE DISCARDS TO HELP PLAN YOUR DEFENSE.
2. A FAILURE TO CASH A WINNER IN A SITUATION WHERE IT SHOULD BE CASHED, INDICATES A LACK OF THAT PARTICULAR WINNER.
3. ONCE IT CAN BE DETERMINED THAT NO TRICKS ARE AVAILABLE IN THE SIDE SUITS, LOOK TO THE TRUMP SUIT FOR EXTRA TRICKS. THIS FREQUENTLY MEANS GIVING DECLARER THE DREADED RUFF AND A SLUFF.
4. WHEN A POSSIBLE TRUMP HONOR IN PARTNER'S HAND CAN BE USED TO "UPPERCUT" DECLARER AND PROMOTE AN EXTRA TRUMP TRICK FOR YOU, DON'T WORRY ABOUT GIVING DECLARER THAT DREADED RUFF AND A SLUFF.

(48) ELEMENTARY

North-South vulnerable
Dealer East

                    North
                    ♠ A 6
                    ♡ 9 7
                    ◇ Q J 10 9 7 4 2
                    ♣ A Q 2
                                        East (you)
                                        ♠ J 2
                                        ♡ Q 10 8 6 4 2
                                        ◇ A K 3
                                        ♣ 10 4

East	South	West	North
2 ♡*	2 NT	Pass	3 NT
All Pass			

*Weak Two
Opening lead: ♡ J

1. Which heart do you play at trick one?
2. You play the queen which holds, what do you return?

ELEMENTARY   (Solution)

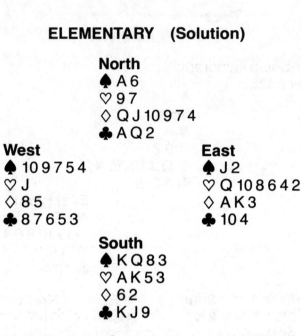

North
♠ A 6
♡ 9 7
♢ Q J 10 9 7 4
♣ A Q 2

West
♠ 10 9 7 5 4
♡ J
♢ 8 5
♣ 8 7 6 5 3

East
♠ J 2
♡ Q 10 8 6 4 2
♢ A K 3
♣ 10 4

South
♠ K Q 8 3
♡ A K 5 3
♢ 6 2
♣ K J 9

1. If you didn't play the ♡ Q at trick one, you had better train yourself to watch the spot cards more closely. Partner may not have another heart and you can knock out both of declarer's heart stoppers before he knocks out your diamond stoppers if you overtake.
2. Return the ♡ 10. If you return a lower heart (ugh), declarer can ride it to dummy's ♡ 9. Notice that if you had the ♡ 5 instead of the ♡ 6, you could not afford to overtake because declarer's ♡ 6 would stand up as a third round trick.

KEY LESSON POINTERS

1. NEVER, NEVER, SIGNAL ENCOURAGEMENT IF YOU CAN AFFORD TO OVERTAKE PARTNER'S CARD. NO MATTER HOW PLEASED YOU ARE WITH PARTNER'S LEAD, PARTNER MAY NOT BE ABLE TO CONTINUE THE SUIT FOR THE OBVIOUS REASON—HE MAY NOT HAVE ONE!
2. A DIRECT OVERCALL OF A WEAK TWO OPENING WITH 2 NT GENERALLY SHOWS THE STRENGTH OF AN OPENING ONE NOTRUMP BID.
3. IT NEVER HURTS TO KNOW DECLARER'S STRENGTH, ALTHOUGH AT TIMES IT CAN BE DEPRESSING.

(49)   THE HIGH TRUMP

North-South vulnerable
Dealer South

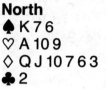

North
♠ K 7 6
♡ A 10 9
◇ Q J 10 7 6 3
♣ 2

East (you)
♠ A 5 2
♡ 7 5 2
◇ A 8 4
♣ Q J 9 8

South	West	North	East
1 ♠	Pass	2 ◇	Pass
2 NT*	Pass	3 ♠	Pass
4 ♠	All Pass		

*15-17
Opening lead: ◇2

Dummy plays low, what is your plan?

THE HIGH TRUMP (Solution)

North
♠ K 7 6
♡ A 10 9
◇ Q J 10 7 6 3
♣ 2

West
♠ 9 3
♡ K J 8 6
◇ 2
♣ 10 7 6 5 4 3

East
♠ A 5 2
♡ 7 5 2
◇ A 8 4
♣ Q J 9 8

South
♠ Q J 10 8 4
♡ Q 4 3
◇ K 9 5
♣ A K

This problem presents a recurring theme—setting up a side suit trick BEFORE giving partner a ruff.

You know from the bidding that partner has only two trumps so you can only give partner one diamond ruff. As you have the ace of trumps, there is no real rush to give partner the ruff. Better to try to establish a heart trick. If partner has the ♡KJ, you must lead a heart before the ace of spades is driven out.

Win the ace of diamonds and shift to a heart. Upon winning the ♠ A, give partner a diamond ruff and hope he can cash a heart trick or the club ace.

KEY LESSON POINTERS

1. THE BIDDING USUALLY REVEALS THE TRUMP COUNT.
2. WHEN PARTNER LEADS A KNOWN SINGLETON TO YOUR ACE AND YOU HAVE THE ACE OF TRUMPS IT MIGHT BE RIGHT TO TRY TO BUILD UP A SIDE-SUIT TRICK BEFORE GIVING PARTNER A RUFF, PARTICULARLY IF PARTNER CAN ONLY RUFF ONCE.
3. TO ALTER THE ABOVE HAND SLIGHTLY, ASSUME YOU HAVE A DOUBLETON ACE OF TRUMPS AND ONE MORE HEART. NOW IT IS RIGHT TO RETURN A DIAMOND IMMEDIATELY, AS YOU CAN GIVE PARTNER A SECOND RUFF UPON WINNING THE ♠ A.

(50) NOW WHAT?

North-South vulnerable
Dealer South

North
♠ K 5 3
♡ A 2
◇ A 9 6 4 2
♣ K 4 3

East (you)
♠ A Q 8 7
♡ J 4 3
◇ K J
♣ J 10 9 5

South	West	North	East
2 ♡*	Pass	4 ♡	All Pass

*Weak
Opening lead: ♠ J

　　Declarer plays low from dummy and you signal with the
♠ 8. At trick two partner continues with the ♠ 2 to the king and
ace, declarer following with the four and six.
1. What do you make of the spade suit?
2. What do you return at trick three, why?

NOW WHAT?   (Solution)

North
♠ K 5 3
♡ A 2
◇ A 9 6 4 2
♣ K 4 3

West
♠ J 10 9 2
♡ 7 6
◇ Q 8 5 3
♣ Q 7 2

East
♠ A Q 8 7
♡ J 4 3
◇ K J
♣ J 10 9 5

South
♠ 6 4
♡ K Q 10 9 8 5
◇ 10 7
♣ A 8 6

1. Declarer must have a small doubleton. If partner had a doubleton, declarer with 10 9xx would have covered the opening lead.
2. You must think in terms of high cards and declarer's probable minor suit distributions. For openers, if partner has the club ace even your aunt Sadie can defeat the contract, so give that card to the declarer.

   If declarer has three diamonds and two clubs, it depends upon who has the ◇ Q. If declarer has it, he will make the hand (unless he has Q10x and takes two finesses into you).

   If declarer started with four clubs and a singleton diamond, your best defense is a trump to prevent a fourth round club ruff in dummy. However if declarer has that hand, partner will uppercut dummy on the fourth club leaving declarer with an awful trump guess if he happens to have: ♠ xx ♡ KQ10xxx ◇ x ♣ Axxx.

   The distribution you really have to guard against is the one you see. Declarer's plan will be to set up the diamond suit for a club discard by ducking a diamond, using the ♡ A and then the ♣ K as entry cards. If you attack the club entry at once by shifting to the ♣ J, and later leading another club upon winning your diamond trick, you kill the entry to the diamond suit and defeat the hand.

KEY LESSON POINTERS

1. ATTACKING SIDE SUIT ENTRIES AS QUICKLY AS POSSIBLE IS A WONDERFUL WAY TO PUT DUMMY'S LONG BROKEN SIDE SUIT TO SLEEP.

(51)   YOUR LUCKY DAY?

North-South vulnerable
Dealer West

                North
                ♠ 7 2
                ♡ A K 5
                ◊ 4 3
                ♣ K Q J 10 4 3

West (you)
♠ Q J 10 9 8
♡ J 10 9
◊ A 10 8 2
♣ A

West	North	East	South
1 ♠	2 ♣	Pass	2 NT
Pass	3 NT	All Pass	

Opening lead: ♠ Q

Declarer wins the ♠ K, partner playing the ♠ 3. At trick two the ♣ 7 is led to your ♣ A, partner playing the ♣ 6.

What do you lead to trick three?

YOUR LUCKY DAY? (Solution)

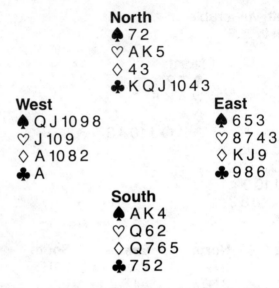

North
♠ 7 2
♡ A K 5
◇ 4 3
♣ K Q J 10 4 3

West
♠ Q J 10 9 8
♡ J 10 9
◇ A 10 8 2
♣ A

East
♠ 6 5 3
♡ 8 7 4 3
◇ K J 9
♣ 9 8 6

South
♠ A K 4
♡ Q 6 2
◇ Q 7 6 5
♣ 7 5 2

A low diamond. Count tricks. Declarer has both the
♠AK (partner played the ♠3), five clubs and at least
two hearts for a grand total of nine.

In order to defeat this contract you must find your
partner with some diamond strength, specifically, K J 9
or K Jxx. Go for it.

Partner wins your diamond lead and continues with
the ◇ J. You collect four diamond tricks regardless of
how declarer plays.

KEY LESSON POINTERS

1. WHEN IT IS CLEAR THAT THE OPPONENTS
   HAVE ENOUGH TRICKS OUTSIDE OF A PAR-
   TICULAR SUIT TO MAKE THEIR CONTRACT, IT IS
   ALMOST ALWAYS RIGHT TO ATTACK THAT PAR-
   TICULAR SUIT.
2. WHEN YOU LEAD AN HONOR IN ONE SUIT AND
   SHIFT TO A LOW CARD IN A SECOND SUIT, YOU
   WANT THE SECOND SUIT RETURNED.

(52)   YOU HAVE FOUR TENS

East-West vulnerable
Dealer South

North
♠ 7 6 4
♡ J 5
♢ 9 8 4
♣ A Q J 9 8

West (you)
♠ A K Q 10
♡ 10 9
♢ 10 7 6 5 3 2
♣ 10

South	West	North	East
1 NT	Pass	2 NT	Pass
3 NT	All Pass		

Opening lead: ♠ A (demands count)

Partner plays the ♠ 8 and declarer the ♠ 9.

1. What do you make of the spade situation?
2. What do you play to trick two?

YOU HAVE FOUR TENS   (Solution)

North
♠ 7 6 4
♡ J 5
◇ 9 8 4
♣ A Q J 9 8

West
♠ A K Q 10
♡ 10 9
◇ 10 7 6 5 3 2
♣ 10

East
♠ 8 5
♡ 8 7 4 3 2
◇ A Q
♣ 6 5 3 2

South
♠ J 9 3 2
♡ A K Q 6
◇ K J
♣ K 7 4

Partner must have a doubleton. He can't have 8532 and declarer J 9. With that holding, partner would have played the ♠ 5 at trick one. (Second highest from four small when giving count.)

You must try to get partner in for a spade lead through declarer. If partner has the ♣ K, he will always get in as declarer will surely have to develop that suit. Therefore, a club lead is out.

Consider the diamond suit. If partner has as little as one diamond declarer cannot have more than three diamond tricks. If declarer has the ♣ K and three diamond tricks he will still have to play hearts to make nine tricks. Therefore, you do not have to shift to a heart. There is time.

Shift to a highish diamond just in case declarer has nine tricks between clubs and hearts. (We have already seen he is unlikely to have nine tricks between clubs and diamonds.) The ◇ A can get away but the ♡ ace can't. The ◇ shift with the ♠ through defeats the contract one trick.

KEY LESSON POINTERS

1. UNDER THE LEAD OF AN ACE VS. A NOTRUMP CONTRACT, THIRD HAND UNBLOCKS ANY HONOR (JACK OR HIGHER), LACKING AN HONOR HE GIVES COUNT. (LOW FROM ODD, SECOND HIGH FROM FOUR, TOP OF A DOUBLETON.)
2. WHEN TRYING TO FIND PARTNER WITH A QUICK ENTRY, DO NOT CONCERN YOURSELF WITH LONG STRONG SUITS THAT DECLARER MUST PLAY IN ANY EVENT.

(53)   THE INFERENCE

North-South vulnerable
Dealer North

North
♠ A Q 8 4
♡ 2
◇ K J 10 9 6
♣ Q 7 4

East (you)
♠ J 7
♡ A 6 5
◇ A 8 5 3 2
♣ K 6 3

North	East	South	West
1 ◇	Pass	1 ♡	Pass
1 ♠	Pass	3 ♡	All Pass

Opening lead: ♠ 3

The ♠ Q wins and a heart is led to the jack and partner's queen. Partner exits with the ♠ 2 to dummy's ace. At trick four, declarer leads a spade from dummy.
1. What do you play?
2. You discard a diamond and declarer ruffs. Declarer exits with the ♡ K, partner follows, and you win. What do you play and what is your plan?

THE INFERENCE   (Solution)

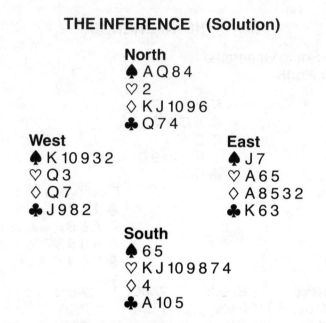

North
♠ A Q 8 4
♡ 2
◇ K J 10 9 6
♣ Q 7 4

West
♠ K 10 9 3 2
♡ Q 3
◇ Q 7
♣ J 9 8 2

East
♠ J 7
♡ A 6 5
◇ A 8 5 3 2
♣ K 6 3

South
♠ 6 5
♡ K J 10 9 8 7 4
◇ 4
♣ A 10 5

The ◇ A. This is one of the more difficult hands. Declarer is known to hold two spades and at least six hearts, perhaps seven. Declarer is also marked with the ♣ A for his invitational jump—where else can his strength be? Furthermore, it is almost certain that declarer has a singleton (or void) in diamonds. Had partner a singleton he probably would have led or shifted to it upon winning the heart queen. What does it all mean?

It means that you should cash the ◇ A removing declarer's later exit card and then play a heart. Declarer is now stuck in his hand and must lose two club tricks for down one. If you play a heart first, declarer wins and exits with a diamond to the jack. You can no longer defeat the contract.

KEY LESSON POINTERS

1. REMOVING AN EXIT CARD FROM DELCARER SO THAT HE CANNOT FORCE YOU TO MAKE A SELF-DAMAGING RE-TURN IS A RATHER NEAT DEFENSIVE STRATAGEM.
2. JUMP REBIDS PROMISE SIX OR SEVEN CARD SUITS, USU-ALLY SIX.
3. WHEN THIRD HAND SEES TEN CARDS IN A SIDE SUIT BE-TWEEN HIMSELF AND DUMMY, IT IS MORE LIKELY THAT DECLARER HAS THE SINGLETON THAN PARTNER. MOST PARTNERS LEAD SINGLETONS SOONER OR LATER. THEY JUST CAN'T STAND IT.

(54) LOOKING AHEAD

Neither side vulnerable
Dealer East

North
♠ K Q
♡ 9 3 2
♢ A Q 9 6 2
♣ 5 4 3

East (you)
♠ 10 7 3
♡ A 8 6
♢ K J 10 3
♣ Q 8 7

East	South	West	North
Pass	1 ♡	Pass	2 ♢
Pass	2 ♡	Pass	3 ♡
Pass	4 ♡	All Pass	

Opening lead: ♡ 4

1. Do you win this trick? If so, what do you return? If not, why not?

LOOKING AHEAD (Solution)

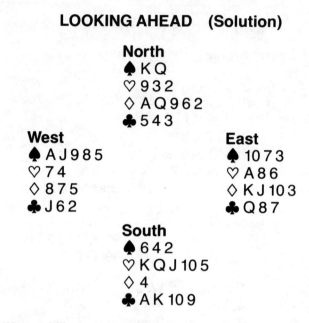

North
♠ K Q
♡ 9 3 2
♢ A Q 9 6 2
♣ 5 4 3

West
♠ A J 9 8 5
♡ 7 4
♢ 8 7 5
♣ J 6 2

East
♠ 10 7 3
♡ A 8 6
♢ K J 10 3
♣ Q 8 7

South
♠ 6 4 2
♡ K Q J 10 5
♢ 4
♣ A K 10 9

When a defender has dummy's long suit bottled up, he should think in terms of preventing declarer from using dummy's trumps for ruffing.

However, with Axx of trumps if you play ace and a trump you may not be able to remove dummy's third trump. Partner probably has a doubleton trump, (singleton trump leads are rare) and a side entry. Therefore, in order to maintain communication with partner's hand, it is better to duck the opening lead. This allows you to eventually play three rounds of trumps instead of two. It also defeats the hand as declarer must lose two spades, a club and a trump.

KEY LESSON POINTERS

1. SINGLETON TRUMP LEADS ARE RARE. WHEN IN DOUBT AS-SUME PARTNER HAS A DOUBLETON.
2. HOLDING Axx IN THE TRUMP SUIT AND NO CERTAIN SIDE ENTRY, ENTERTAIN THE THOUGHT OF DUCKING PARTNER'S TRUMP LEAD. IF PARTNER HAS AN EARLY ENTRY YOU MAY BE ABLE TO PLAY THREE ROUNDS OF TRUMPS INSTEAD OF TWO.
3. WHEN YOU HAVE DUMMY'S LONG SUIT UNDER CONTROL, OR HAVE REASON TO BELIEVE PARTNER HAS IT UNDER CONTROL, THE BEST DEFENSE IS OFTEN TRUMP LEADS PREVENTING DE-CLARER FROM RUFFING IN THE SHORTER TRUMP HAND. THE LOSERS IN THE SIDE SUITS WON'T RUN AWAY.

(55) TWO DEUCES

Neither side vulnerable
Dealer South

North
♠ J 10 8 7 6 3
♡ K
◇ K J 10 4
♣ 10 4

West (you)
♠ 2
♡ Q J 9 4
◇ A 7 6 5
♣ A Q 7 2

South	West	North	East
1 ♠*	Dbl.	4 ♠	All Pass

*Five card suit
Opening lead: ♡ Q

At trick one partner plays the ♡2. At trick two the ◇J is led from dummy, partner playing the ◇2 and declarer the ◇Q.

1. Do you win this trick? If so, why? If not, why not?
2. Assuming you win the trick, what do you return at trick three?

TWO DEUCES (Solution)

North
♠ J 10 8 7 6 3
♡ K
◇ K J 10 4
♣ 10 4

West
♠ 2
♡ Q J 9 4
◇ A 7 6 5
♣ A Q 7 2

East
♠ A
♡ 7 6 5 3 2
◇ 8 3 2
♣ J 6 5 3

South
♠ K Q 9 5 4
♡ A 10 8
◇ Q 9
♣ K 9 8

1. Yes, you should win this trick! Do you want declarer discarding a club from dummy on the ace of hearts?
2. A trump! Why didn't declarer come to his hand with a trump to discard a club upon the ♡A? Because he doesn't have the ace of trumps, that's why. Partner's club return after winning the ♠A defeats the hand one trick.

KEY LESSON POINTERS

1. WHENEVER DECLARER SEEMS TO HAVE AN OVERABUNDANCE OF TRUMPS AND DOES NOT PLAY THE SUIT THERE IS USUALLY A REASON. ONE REASON MAY BE NOT TO GIVE UP THE LEAD AT THAT MOMENT. IN OTHER WORDS, HE HAS A TRUMP LOSER.
2. WHENEVER A SINGLETON KING WINS THE FIRST TRICK AT A SUIT CONTRACT, THE DEFENDERS MUST BE CAREFUL ABOUT ALLOWING THE DECLARER TO GET TO THE OPPOSITE HAND TO TAKE A DISCARD ON THE ACE.
3. TAKE TIME TO FIND OUT WHETHER OR NOT YOUR OPPONENTS ARE PLAYING FOUR OR FIVE CARD MAJORS. IT MAKES COUNTING THE HAND EASIER.

(56) STRONG PARTNER

East-West vulnerable
Dealer South

North
♠ Q J 4
♡ A Q 10 5 4
◇ 6 5
♣ 10 5 2

West (you)
♠ K 5 3
♡ 8 7 6 2
◇ 9 8
♣ A 9 6 4

South	West	North	East
1 ◇	Pass	1 ♡	Pass
3 ◇	Pass	3 ♠	Pass
4 NT	Pass	5 ◇	All Pass

Opening lead: ♣ A

Partner plays the ♣ 8 and declarer the ♣ K.

1. What does partner's ♣ 8 mean?
2. What do you play at trick two, and why?

STRONG PARTNER   (Solution)

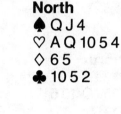

North
♠ Q J 4
♡ A Q 10 5 4
♢ 6 5
♣ 10 5 2

West
♠ K 5 3
♡ 8 7 6 2
♢ 9 8
♣ A 9 6 4

East
♠ 10 9 6 2
♡ 9 3
♢ A 7
♣ Q J 8 7 3

South
♠ A 8 7
♡ K J
♢ K Q J 10 4 3 2
♣ K

1. It is an encouraging signal.
2. The ♡ 2. Go back to the bidding. When South asked
   for aces, he found only one and signed off in 5 ♢.
   North-South are missing two aces. The other ace
   must be the ♢A because partner wouldn't have sig-
   nalled with a high club if he had the ♠A. (After all,
   partner knew that declarer had the ♣K.)
   If partner wins the first trump play and returns a second heart he effectively kills dummy's heart suit and
   you eventually make your ♠K.

KEY LESSON POINTERS

1. WHEN PARTNER GIVES YOU AN ENCOURAGING
   SIGNAL IN ONE SUIT, IT IS UNLIKELY HE CAN
   STAND A LEAD IN ANOTHER. HAD HE WANTED
   ANOTHER SUIT LED, HE WOULD NOT HAVE EN-
   COURAGED YOU IN THE FIRST PLACE.
2. ONE WAY TO KILL A SIDE SUIT IN DUMMY THAT
   HAS NO SIDE ENTRIES IS TO LEAD THE SUIT BE-
   FORE DECLARER CAN DRAW TRUMPS.

(57)   SO QUICK?

Both sides vulnerable
Dealer South

North
♠ A 7 6
♡ Q J 5
◇ Q 7 3 2
♣ J 7 6

East (you)
♠ 8 5 3
♡ 9 8
◇ K J 10 6
♣ 5 4 3 2

South	West	North	East
1 NT	Pass	3 NT	All Pass

Opening lead: ♠ 4

1. Dummy plays low, which spade do you play?
2. Declarer wins the opening lead with the ♠10 and plays a heart to dummy's queen. Which heart do you play?
3. At trick three the ♣ J is led from the table. Which club do you play?

SO QUICK?   (Solution)

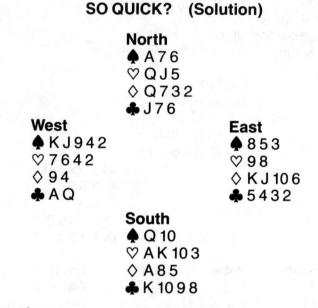

North
♠ A 7 6
♡ Q J 5
◊ Q 7 3 2
♣ J 7 6

West
♠ K J 9 4 2
♡ 7 6 4 2
◊ 9 4
♣ A Q

East
♠ 8 5 3
♡ 9 8
◊ K J 10 6
♣ 5 4 3 2

South
♠ Q 10
♡ A K 10 3
◊ A 8 5
♣ K 10 9 8

1. The ♠ 3. With *three* small (8xx or less) third hand gives partner more information by playing low rather than high. (When the highest card is so small it doesn't force out anything of consequence, so count becomes more important.)
2. The nine to show a doubleton. The weaker hand tends to give more count signals than the stronger hand. In this case, you are the weaker hand.
3. The ♣ 4. Second high from four small to give count.
   The point of this hand is to recognize how your trick one play has helped your partner. Once your partner knows you have three spades he can plunk down the ♠ K upon winning the ♣ Q. If he plays you for a doubleton (he will if you play the ♠ 8 at trick one) he will abandon spades and the hand will be made. Even a diamond shift won't work.

KEY LESSON POINTERS

1. WHEN HOLDING THREE SMALL IN THE SUIT PARTNER HAS LED, PLAY LOW AT TRICK ONE. DO NOT BOTHER WITH THIRD HAND HIGH.
2. GIVING COUNT ON DEFENSE FREQUENTLY HELPS THE DE-CLARER MORE THAN THE DEFENDERS. HOWEVER, BOTH HANDS DO NOT ALWAYS HAVE TO GIVE COUNT. USUALLY THE WEAK HAND GIVES COUNT AND THE STRONG HAND DOES NOT. IT IS THE STRONG HAND THAT MUST KNOW WHAT IS GOING ON. HOWEVER, EVEN THE STRONG HAND GIVES COUNT WHEN DE-CLARER ATTACKS DUMMY'S LONG SUIT AND THERE ARE NO CERTAIN SIDE ENTRIES TO DUMMY.

(58) YARBOROUGH

East-West vulnerable
Dealer West

North
♠ A K Q 10
♡ Q J
♢ A K Q J
♣ 6 5 3

East (you)
♠ 7 6 4
♡ 4
♢ 9 8 6 5 3
♣ 9 8 5 2

West	North	East	South
1 ♡	Dbl.	Pass	1 ♠
2 ♡	3 ♠	Pass	4 ♠
All Pass			

Opening lead: ♡ K

Partner continues with the heart ace, what do you discard?

YARBOROUGH   (Solution)

North
♠ A K Q 10
♡ Q J
♢ A K Q J
♣ 6 5 3

West
♠ 2
♡ A K 10 9 5 3
♢ 10 7 4
♣ A Q 7

East
♠ 7 6 4
♡ 4
♢ 9 8 6 5 3
♣ 9 8 5 2

South
♠ J 9 8 3 2
♡ 8 7 6 2
♢ 2
♣ K J 10

You had better discard a trump if you want to defeat this contract! This will be your last chance to win the lead and those diamonds should look menacing enough to encourage you to ruff and shift to a club. Your partner will love you forever...or at least until the next hand.

KEY LESSON POINTERS

1. DON'T BE AFRAID TO TRUMP YOUR PARTNER'S ACE IF YOU MUST GET THE LEAD AT ONCE.
2. TRUMPING PARTNER'S ACE ALWAYS MAKES FOR GOOD COPY EVEN IF IT DOESN'T WORK.

(59) NARY A JACK

Both sides vulnerable
Dealer South

North
♠ J 10 9 4
♡ A 7 3
◊ Q J 4 3 2
♣ 10

East (you)
♠ Q 7 6
♡ Q J 5
◊ K 10 9
♣ A 8 3 2

South	West	North	East
1 NT	Pass	2 ♣	Pass
2 ♡	Pass	2 NT	All Pass

Opening lead: ♣ 5

1. You win the ♣ A, declarer playing the ♣ 6. What do you return?
2. You return the ♣ 2, declarer plays the ♣ 9, partner the ♣ J and dummy discards the ♡ 3. Partner plays the ♣ K, dummy discards a low diamond, and you, which club do you play?
3. You unblock the ♣ 8 and declarer follows with the ♣ Q. Partner continues with the ♣ 7, dummy throws another diamond and declarer a heart. At trick five partner cashes the fifth (and last) club, dummy discards a second low heart. What do you discard?

NARY A JACK   (Solution)

North
♠ J 10 9 4
♡ A 7 3
◇ Q J 4 3 2
♣ 10

West
♠ 8 3 2
♡ 10 6 4
◇ 8 7
♣ K J 7 5 4

East
♠ Q 7 6
♡ Q J 5
◇ K 10 9
♣ A 8 3 2

South
♠ A K 5
♡ K 9 8 2
◇ A 6 5
♣ Q 9 6

There are three important features to this hand. (1) Returning the ♣ 2 at trick two, your original fourth best, to give partner a count on the clubs; (2) unblocking the ♣ 8 so partner can run his clubs in peace; (3) realizing partner cannot have as much as a side jack and discarding a heart hoping partner has the ♡ 10. You are sort of squeezed in three suits.

KEY LESSON POINTERS

1. IN MOST CASES RETURN YOUR ORIGINAL FOURTH BEST IN PARTNER'S SUIT.
2. BE WARY OF UNBLOCKING ON THE THIRD ROUND OF THE SUIT IF YOUR SECOND HIGHEST CARD COULD BLOCK THE RUN OF THE SUIT. (THE SECOND HIGHEST CARD WILL USUALLY BE HIGHER THAN AN EIGHT).
3. ADD YOUR POINTS TO DUMMY'S AND ADD THAT TOTAL TO DECLARER'S AVERAGE COUNT TO DETERMINE PARTNER'S STRENGTH. IN THIS CASE DECLARER HAVING PASSED AN INVITATIONAL RAISE MUST BE MINIMUM. ASSUMING A 15-17 NOTRUMP RANGE, DECLARER'S PASS INDICATED EITHER 15 OR 16 WITH 4-3-3-3 DISTRIBUTION.

(60) FENCES

Neither side vulnerable
Dealer East

North
♠ 10 4 3 2
♡ Q 10
◇ K 8 7 4 2
♣ K J

East (you)
♠ A J
♡ K J 8 7 6
◇ J 5
♣ A 7 4 2

East	South	West	North
1 ♡	2 ◇	2 ♡	4 ◇*
All Pass			

*Preemptive
Opening lead: ♠ 9

   You win the ♠ A and declarer plays the ♠ K. What do you play to trick two?

FENCES   (Solution)

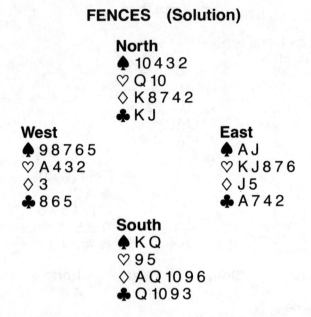

North
♠ 10 4 3 2
♡ Q 10
◇ K 8 7 4 2
♣ K J

West
♠ 9 8 7 6 5
♡ A 4 3 2
◇ 3
♣ 8 6 5

East
♠ A J
♡ K J 8 7 6
◇ J 5
♣ A 7 4 2

South
♠ K Q
♡ 9 5
◇ A Q 10 9 6
♣ Q 10 9 3

The ♡ K! Partner must have at least one face card for his single raise and it is probably the ♡ A. Good players are reluctant to lead aces (even in partner's suit) for fear of setting up a possible king in declarer's hand.

There is a danger that declarer will be able to park one of his losing hearts on the ♠ 10, so you should attack that suit at once.

The reason you lead the king rather than fourth best is that partner may think he has struck gold (finding you with the lone ♠ A), and try to give you a spade ruff.

After you collect two heart tricks the club ace becomes the setting trick.

KEY LESSON POINTERS

1. THERE ARE THREE MAIN REASONS WHY PARTNER MAY NOT LEAD YOUR SUIT EVEN THOUGH HE HAS SUPPORTED IT:
   (1) HE HAS THE ACE.
   (2) HE HAS A STRONG HONOR SEQUENCE IN ANOTHER SUIT.
   (3) HE IS TRYING FOR A RUFF IN ANOTHER SUIT.
   IT IS YOUR JOB TO FIGURE OUT WHICH.
2. GOOD DEFENDERS TRY TO ANTICIPATE THEIR PARTNER'S PROBLEMS AND MAKE LIFE EASIER FOR THEM. THE BEST OF DEFENDERS CAN GO WRONG AT TIMES. IF ONE HAND KNOWS THE RIGHT DEFENSE, THAT HAND MUST TAKE CHARGE.

(61)   WHICH WAY?

Both sides vulnerable
Dealer South

North
♠ J 9 8 4
♡ Q 10 9 3
◇ Q J 10
♣ 8 4

East (you)
♠ 7 3
♡ A 2
◇ A 7 6 4 2
♣ J 10 9 7

South	West	North	East
2 ♣*	Pass	2 ◇**	Pass
2 NT***	Pass	3 ♣****	Pass
3 ♠	Pass	4 ♠	All Pass

   * Strong and artificial
  ** Waiting bid
 *** 23-24 balanced
**** Stayman
     Opening lead: ◇8

1. Which card do you play to the first trick? Why?
2. You win and declarer plays the king. What do you return?

WHICH WAY?   (Solution)

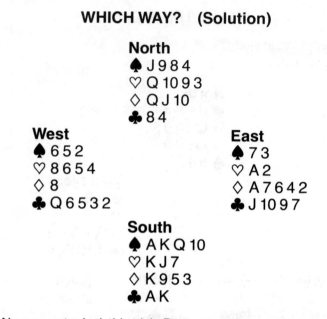

North
♠ J 9 8 4
♡ Q 10 9 3
♢ Q J 10
♣ 8 4

West
♠ 6 5 2
♡ 8 6 5 4
♢ 8
♣ Q 6 5 3 2

East
♠ 7 3
♡ A 2
♢ A 7 6 4 2
♣ J 10 9 7

South
♠ A K Q 10
♡ K J 7
♢ K 9 5 3
♣ A K

1. No reason to duck this trick. Partner may have a singleton.
2. The ♢ 7. You should give up on trying for a heart ruff. In order for that to succeed partner must have the ♡ K. (If partner has the ♠ K, declarer won't take a finesse if he fears a ruff). Count the points. You have 9 and dummy 6 for a total of 15. Declarer has at least 23 for a total of 38, so partner cannot have more than two. Your best chance is to hope partner has a singleton diamond. Careful! Return the 7, your highest, to ask for a heart return.

KEY LESSON POINTERS

1. BEFORE GOING FOR A RUFF OF YOUR OWN, MAKE SURE PARTNER CAN HAVE THE CARD(S) YOU NEED TO GET THE RUFF.
2. DON'T BE LAZY. ADD YOUR HIGH CARD POINTS TO DUMMY'S AND THE TOTAL TO DECLARER'S TO DETERMINE HOW MANY HIGH CARD POINTS PARTNER HAS.
3. WHEN GIVING PARTNER A RUFF, OR WHEN YOU THINK YOU MIGHT BE GIVING PARTNER A RUFF, TELL YOUR PARTNER BY THE SIZE OF THE CARD YOU LEAD WHICH SUIT YOU WANT RETURNED. A HIGH SPOT CARD ASKS FOR THE HIGHER RANKING OF THE TWO SIDE SUITS, AND A LOW SPOT CARD FOR THE LOWER RANKING. IF YOU HAVE NO PREFERENCE, LEAD A MIDDLE SPOT CARD AND WATCH PARTNER SUFFER TRYING TO WORK IT OUT.

(62)   FRIENDLY LEAD!

Both sides vulnerable
Dealer West

North
♠ K Q 10 3
♡ J
♢ 8 7 6 5
♣ 8 7 6 5

East (you)
♠ 9 8 5
♡ 6 5
♢ A 9 4
♣ Q J 4 3 2

West	North	East	South
1 ♠	Pass	2 ♠	4 ♡
All Pass			

Opening lead: ♠ A

1. Which spade do you play? Why?
2. Assume you play the ♠ 9 and partner switches to the ♢ 2 which you win declarer playing the ♢ 3. What do you return at trick three?

FRIENDLY LEAD!   (Solution)

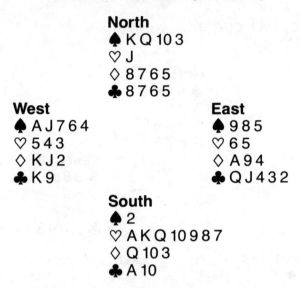

North
♠ K Q 10 3
♡ J
◇ 8 7 6 5
♣ 8 7 6 5

West
♠ A J 7 6 4
♡ 5 4 3
◇ K J 2
♣ K 9

East
♠ 9 8 5
♡ 6 5
◇ A 9 4
♣ Q J 4 3 2

South
♠ 2
♡ A K Q 10 9 8 7
◇ Q 10 3
♣ A 10

You should play the ♠ 9 as a suit preference play. You couldn't possibly want a spade continuation, nor could you be short suited.

When partner returns a *low* diamond he wants that suit returned. If partner had wanted a club switch he would have led a higher diamond indicating weakness in the diamond suit.

KEY LESSON POINTERS

1. WHEN PARTNER LEADS AN ACE IN A SUIT THAT HAS BEEN SUPPORTED, AND THAT LEAD ESTABLISHES A NUMBER OF DISCARDS FOR DECLARER, THIRD HAND GIVES SUIT PREFERENCE.
2. WHEN PARTNER SWITCHES TO A LOW CARD HE WANTS THAT SUIT RETURNED. HAD HE WANTED ANOTHER SUIT RETURNED HE WOULD HAVE SWITCHED TO A HIGHER CARD.

(63)   HANGING IN THERE

Neither side vulnerable
Dealer East

North
♠ 8 6 2
♡ J 5 3
◇ A 9 4 3
♣ 9 8 6

East (you)
♠ A 10 7 5
♡ 10 8 6
◇ 5
♣ K Q 10 4 2

East	South	West	North
Pass	1 NT	All Pass	

Opening lead: ◇J (Denies a higher honor)

Declarer wins the ◇Q.

1. At trick two declarer leads the ♡Q to partner's ♡K. Who has the ♡A?
2. Partner shifts to the ♠Q. Which spade do you play?
3. Assume you win the trick. What do you return, and why?

HANGING IN THERE   (Solution)

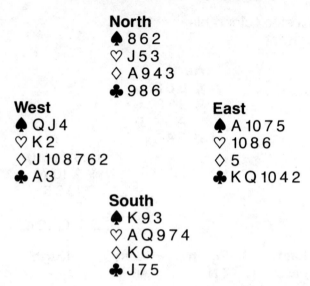

North
♠ 8 6 2
♡ J 5 3
◇ A 9 4 3
♣ 9 8 6

West
♠ Q J 4
♡ K 2
◇ J 10 8 7 6 2
♣ A 3

East
♠ A 10 7 5
♡ 10 8 6
◇ 5
♣ K Q 10 4 2

South
♠ K 9 3
♡ A Q 9 7 4
◇ K Q
♣ J 7 5

1. Declarer. If he did not have the ♡A he would have started by leading low to the jack.

3. A low club. Declarer is marked with the ◇KQ, ♡AQ, and ♠ K for a total of eight tricks as well as 14 high card points in those three suits. Partner must have the ♣ A. Lead a low club so you don't block the suit. You do need five club tricks to defeat this hand, you know.

KEY LESSON POINTERS

1. WHEN PARTNER LEADS AN HONOR CARD VS. NO-TRUMP YOU SHOULD KNOW WHERE THE MISSING HONORS ARE.
2. WHEN DECLARER ATTACKS A SUIT, YOU CAN SOME-TIMES INFER BY THE MANNER IN WHICH HE AT-TACKS THE SUIT WHERE THE MISSING HONORS ARE.
3. KEEP TRACK OF DECLARER'S POINT COUNT IN RE-LATIONSHIP TO HIS BIDDING.
4. BE CAREFUL ABOUT BLOCKING SUITS WHERE YOU AND PARTNER HAVE THE HIGH HONORS.

(64) PREEMPTS

East-West vuln.
Dealer South

North
♠ J
♡ A 9 7
♢ A J 9 7 4 3
♣ A 8 6

West (you)
♠ A 10 5
♡ 10 8 6
♢ K Q 10 8
♣ K 9 7

South	West	North	East
3 ♠	Pass	4 ♠	All Pass

Opening lead: ♢ K

Declarer wins in dummy, partner playing the ♢ 2, declarer the ♢ 5.

1. Who has the missing diamond? Declarer continues with the ♠ J from dummy, partner playing the ♠ 4.
2. Do you take this trick? Assume you win the trick, what do you play to trick three?

PREEMPTS   (Solution)

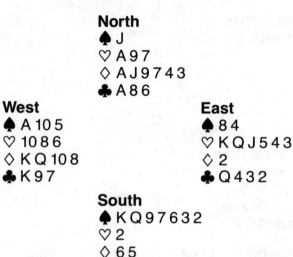

North
♠ J
♡ A 9 7
◇ A J 9 7 4 3
♣ A 8 6

West
♠ A 10 5
♡ 10 8 6
◇ K Q 10 8
♣ K 9 7

East
♠ 8 4
♡ K Q J 5 4 3
◇ 2
♣ Q 4 3 2

South
♠ K Q 9 7 6 3 2
♡ 2
◇ 6 5
♣ J 10 5

1. Declarer. If partner had a doubleton he would have started an echo.
2. The ◇8 allowing partner to trump, thus killing the diamond suit. If you do not make this play, declarer can win your heart return (say) ruff a heart, draw trumps and lead up to the ◇J for a later club discard. It also doesn't work to attack clubs given the layout of the suit.

   After partner ruffs your diamond return and exits with a heart, declarer must lose two club tricks against best defense.

KEY LESSON POINTERS

1. WHEN THE KING IS LED AND THE DUMMY COMES DOWN WITH THE AJ(x)(x), THIRD HAND HIGH-LOWS WITH A DOUBLETON. OTHERWISE THIRD HAND GIVES COUNT BUT ONLY IF HE (1) HAS SUPPORTED THE SUIT: (2) DECLARER HAS BID TWO OTHER SUITS: (3) THE OPPONENTS ARE PLAYING AT THE FIVE OR SIX LEVEL.
2. KILLING A DISCARD EARLY IS A PLAY THAT MANY DEFENDERS OVERLOOK.

(65)   SEE IT?

North-South vulnerable
Dealer South

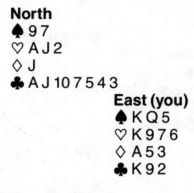

North
♠ 9 7
♡ A J 2
♦ J
♣ A J 10 7 5 4 3

East (you)
♠ K Q 5
♡ K 9 7 6
♦ A 5 3
♣ K 9 2

South	West	North	East
1 NT*	Pass	3 NT	All Pass

* 12-14
Opening lead: ♠ 4

   You play the ♠Q which holds, declarer playing the ♠2.
At trick two you play the ♠K, declarer playing the ♠10 and
partner the ♠J.
1. What does the ♠J signify?
2. What do you play at trick three?
3. You play your remaining spade to declarer's ace and part-
    ner's three, dummy discarding a low heart. At trick four
    declarer runs the ♣Q, partner playing the ♣6. How do
    you defend?

SEE IT?   (Solution)

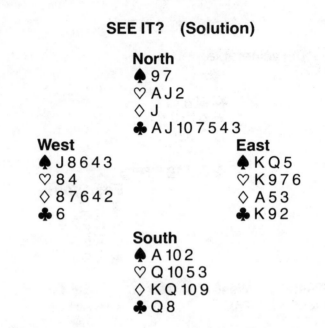

North
♠ 9 7
♡ A J 2
◇ J
♣ A J 10 7 5 4 3

West
♠ J 8 6 4 3
♡ 8 4
◇ 8 7 6 4 2
♣ 6

East
♠ K Q 5
♡ K 9 7 6
◇ A 5 3
♣ K 9 2

South
♠ A 10 2
♡ Q 10 5 3
◇ K Q 10 9
♣ Q 8

1. It indicates that partner has equivalent lower spades, but no spade higher.
2. You are in the driver's seat. Can you see it? Cash the ◇ A, and throw dummy in with the ♣ 9. Now sit back and wait for the ♡ K, the setting trick.

KEY LESSON POINTERS

1. AFTER LEADING LOW FROM A KNOWN LONG SUIT, PART-NER'S LATER PLAY OF AN UNNECESSARILY HIGH CARD (USUALLY AN HONOR) INDICATES NO HIGHER HONOR, BUT THE LOWER EQUIVALENT CARDS. FOR EXAMPLE,

North (dummy)
♠ 9 4

West
♠ 10 8 7 3 2

East
♠ K Q 5

South
♠ A J 6

AT NOTRUMP WEST LEADS THE ♠ 3 TO THE ♠ Q AND ♠ 6. WEST CONTINUES WITH THE ♠ K TO THE ♠ A. AT THIS POINT WEST PLAYS THE ♠ 10 DENYING THE ♠ J.
2. BE ON THE LOOKOUT FOR THROW-IN PLAYS WHICH FORCE THE OPPONENTS TO LEAD SUITS TO YOU RATHER THAN VICE VERSA.

(66)   LOUSY HAND

North-South vulnerable
Dealer East

North
♠ J 10 9 6 5
♡ A 4
♢ K 9 8 7
♣ K 4

East (you)
♠ 7 3
♡ Q 8 6 5
♢ J 2
♣ J 9 8 7 2

East	South	West	North
Pass	1 ♠	2 ♡	3 ♡
4 ♡	4 ♠	5 ♡	5 ♠
All Pass			

Opening lead: ♡ 10 (Zero or two higher honors)

Dummy wins with the ace as you signal with the ♡ 8. Declarer draws two rounds of trumps, partner discarding the ♡ 7 and the ♡ 3.

Next, declarer plays the ♣ A K, partner contributing the ♣ 6 and the ♣ 3.

1. A low heart is led from dummy. Which heart do you play? Why?
2. You play the queen and everyone follows, what do you play now?

LOUSY HAND   (Solution)

North
♠ J 10 9 6 5
♡ A 4
◇ K 9 8 7
♣ K 4

West
♠ —
♡ K J 10 7 3
◇ A 10 6 5
♣ Q 10 6 3

East
♠ 7 3
♡ Q 8 6 5
◇ J 2
♣ J 9 8 7 2

South
♠ A K Q 8 4 2
♡ 9 2
◇ Q 4 3
♣ A 5

1. The ♡Q. If declarer ruffs it doesn't matter, but if declarer has a second heart it is important that you, not partner, break the diamond suit.
2. Counting the hand you discover that declarer has six spades, two hearts, two clubs and therefore, three diamonds. As you need two diamond tricks to defeat the contract partner needs either the ◇ AQ or, with luck, the ◇ A10.

   By leading the ◇J you give declarer a guess. If he plays you for the ◇ 10 he will go down. In order to make the hand declarer must rise with the ◇Q.

   If partner has to break diamonds, there is no hope.

KEY LESSON POINTERS

1. DISCUSS YOUR LEAD CONVENTIONS SO THAT THERE IS NO CONFUSION WHEN AN HONOR IS LED.
2. NO MATTER HOW WEAK YOUR HAND, DO NOT GET LAZY ON DEFENSE. KEEP COUNTING. HERE YOU HAVE A VERY WEAK HAND, YET YOU ARE THE ONE THAT MUST MAKE TWO KEY PLAYS.

(67) CUEING A SINGLETON

Neither side vulnerable
Dealer South

North
♠ A K 8 7 3
♡ 6
◇ 9 4 2
♣ K 5 3 2

West (you)
♠ Q 10 9 4
♡ A K Q 9 5
◇ 10 3
♣ 7 4

South	West	North	East
1 ◇	1 ♡	1 ♠	3 ♡*
4 ◇	Pass	4 ♡	Pass
5 ♣	Pass	6 ◇	All Pass

* Preemptive
Opening lead: ♡ Q (asking for count).

Partner plays the ♡ 2 and declarer the ♡ 4. What do you play to trick two?

CUEING A SINGLETON   (Solution)

North
♠ A K 8 7 3
♡ 6
◊ 9 4 2
♣ K 5 3 2

West
♠ Q 10 9 4
♡ A K Q 9 5
◊ 10 3
♣ 7 4

East
♠ J 2
♡ J 10 7 3 2
◊ 7 6
♣ Q J 10 8

South
♠ 6 5
♡ 8 4
◊ A K Q J 8 5
♣ A 9 6

A high heart. Partner's play to trick one shows an odd number of hearts, certainly five, for his preemptive jump raise.

Declarer cannot realistically have three spades on the bidding, and has promised the ♣ A with his 5 ♣ bid. So where is the setting trick coming from?

The only chance is that declarer has a "slow" club loser which he will try to discard on the spades. In order to frustrate this plan you must attack a dummy entry. That entry is a heart ruff entry. If you lead a second heart, forcing dummy to ruff, (prematurely) declarer will not have the wherewithal (enough entries) to set up the fifth spade for a club discard.

With any other return, declarer makes the slam in a breeze.

KEY LESSON POINTERS

1. LEADING THE QUEEN FROM ACE, KING, QUEEN, HAS THE DISADVANTAGE OF SHOWING DECLARER WHERE THOSE HONORS ARE. IT HAS THE ADVANTAGE OF TELLING PARTNER WHAT YOU HAVE IN THE SUIT AS WELL AS GETTING WHAT MIGHT BE A VALUABLE COUNT SIGNAL AT TRICK ONE.
2. CONSIDER FORCING THE DUMMY TO RUFF WHEN YOU WISH TO PREVENT ESTABLISHMENT OF DUMMY'S LONG SUIT.
3. TAKE TIME OUT AFTER TRICK ONE TO CONSIDER DECLARER'S DISTRIBUTION AND TRY TO VISUALIZE SOME REASONABLE HOLDING THAT GIVES YOU A CHANCE TO DEFEAT THE CONTRACT. IN OTHER WORDS, PLAY FOR SOMETHING.

(68) ROUTINE

North-South vulnerable
Dealer East

North
♠ K Q 4
♡ 10
♢ 5 3
♣ K J 10 9 8 7 6

East (you)
♠ J 10 7 6
♡ K J 9 2
♢ A K 4 2
♣ 3

East	South	West	North
1 ♢	1 ♡	2 ♢	3 ♣
Pass	3 NT	All Pass	

Opening lead: ♢ J

1. Which card do you play at trick one?
2. You win with the king, what do you play at trick two?

ROUTINE   (Solution)

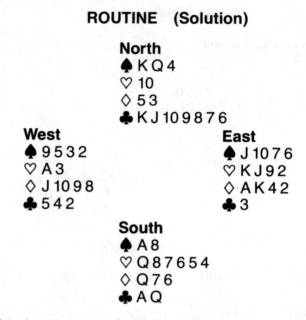

North
♠ K Q 4
♡ 10
◊ 5 3
♣ K J 10 9 8 7 6

West
♠ 9 5 3 2
♡ A 3
◊ J 10 9 8
♣ 5 4 2

East
♠ J 10 7 6
♡ K J 9 2
◊ A K 4 2
♣ 3

South
♠ A 8
♡ Q 8 7 6 5 4
◊ Q 7 6
♣ A Q

1. You should win the trick because there is a grave danger that declarer can rattle off a zillion black suit tricks while you can defeat the hand in the red suits.

2. The ♡ J and continue with a low heart if the jack holds. This defeats the hand at once if partner has the ♡ A. You collect three hearts plus two diamonds. Even if declarer has the ♡ A, you still defeat the contract if partner has a club trick as well as the ♡ Q.

   You should play your partner for at least one high honor outside of the ◊ J. If it is the spade ace there is nothing you can do. However if it is either the ♡ A or the ♣ A along with the ♡ Q you are in clover.

KEY LESSON POINTERS

1. THE MAIN THOUGHT RUNNING THROUGH YOUR MIND ON DEFENSE SHOULD BE: HOW ARE WE GOING TO DEFEAT THIS CONTRACT? IF YOU CAN'T DO IT IN YOUR OWN HAND, GIVE PARTNER THE MINIMUM OUTSIDE STRENGTH NECESSARY, AND PLAY ACCORDINGLY.

2. WHEN HOLDING A KJ9 OR AN AJ9 COMBINATION WITH THE 10 TO YOUR RIGHT, BEGIN BY LEADING THE JACK. IT IS CALLED A "SURROUNDING PLAY." PARTNER WILL UNDERSTAND. HE WILL, HE WILL.

(69) STRANGE

North-South vulnerable
Dealer North

> **North**
> ♠ J 8 7
> ♡ Q 5
> ◊ A K Q 4 2
> ♣ K 4 3

West (you)
♠ K 4 3 2
♡ 4
◊ 10 7 6
♣ Q 8 7 5 2

North	East	South	West
1 ◊	1 ♡	1 NT	Pass
2 NT	Pass	3 NT	All Pass

Opening lead: ♣ 5

Dummy plays the ♣ K, partner the ♣ A, and declarer the ♣ 6. At trick two partner returns the ♣ 10, declarer covers with the ♣ J.
1. Do you win this trick? If not, why not?
2. If so, what do you return at trick three?

STRANGE   (Solution)

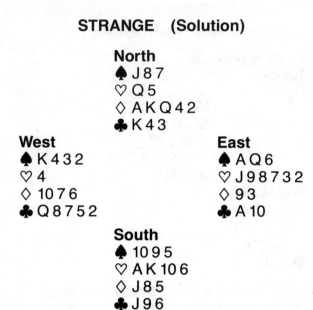

North
♠ J 8 7
♡ Q 5
♢ A K Q 4 2
♣ K 4 3

West
♠ K 4 3 2
♡ 4
♢ 10 7 6
♣ Q 8 7 5 2

East
♠ A Q 6
♡ J 9 8 7 3 2
♢ 9 3
♣ A 10

South
♠ 10 9 5
♡ A K 10 6
♢ J 8 5
♣ J 9 6

1. Yes. What possible reason could you have for ducking?
2. A low spade. You know to do this from declarer's play in the club suit. Playing the king from dummy when holding the jack in one's hand, giving up on a sure stopper, (you might have led from ♣Q10xxx) is done only in desperation. Declarer must be wide open in another suit and can't stand a shift. The suit he fears must be spades, play one.

KEY LESSON POINTERS

1. WHEN DECLARER MAKES AN UNUSUAL PLAY HE MUST HAVE A REASON. DON'T PLAY UNTIL YOU WORK OUT THE REASON.

(70)   THREE CARD JUMP RAISE

North-South vulnerable
Dealer North

North
♠ K Q 2
♡ A K Q J 6
♢ 7 5 2
♣ K Q

West (you)
♠ J 9
♡ 10 7 5 4 3
♢ K Q 10 3
♣ J 9

North	East	South	West
1 ♡	Pass	1 ♠	Pass
3 ♠	Pass	4 ♠	All Pass

Opening lead: ♢K

1. Partner plays the ♢8 and declarer the ♢6. What do you play at trick two?
2. Assume you lead a low diamond to partner's ace. Partner returns a diamond to your queen, declarer following with the jack. What do you play to trick four?

THREE CARD JUMP RAISE   (Solution)

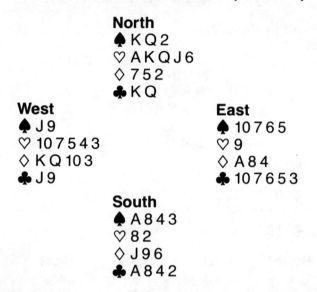

North
♠ K Q 2
♡ A K Q J 6
◇ 7 5 2
♣ K Q

West
♠ J 9
♡ 10 7 5 4 3
◇ K Q 10 3
♣ J 9

East
♠ 10 7 6 5
♡ 9
◇ A 8 4
♣ 10 7 6 5 3

South
♠ A 8 4 3
♡ 8 2
◇ J 9 6
♣ A 8 4 2

A fourth round of diamonds giving declarer a ruff and a sluff.

The reason being that partner cannot have the ♣ A. If he had that card, he would have cashed it before leading his last diamond.

If declarer has the ace of clubs the only chance is to play partner for four spades to the ten. Once you lead the fourth diamond, partner discarding a heart, declarer is in serious trouble. If he ruffs in dummy, partner makes a trump trick; if he ruffs in his hand, partner also makes a trump trick.

If you woodenly exit with a club or a heart, declarer can make the hand if he guesses to finesse the ♠ 8 (the percentage play after cashing the king-queen).

KEY LESSON POINTERS

1. WHEN PLACING THE HIGH CARDS AROUND THE TABLE, ASSUME PARTNER IS DEFENDING LOGICALLY. (PARTNER NOT HAVING THE ♣A BECAUSE HE DIDN'T CASH IT BEFORE LEADING THE THIRD DIAMOND, ETC. ETC.)
2. WHEN THERE ARE NO TRICKS COMING FROM THE SIDE SUITS CONSIDER A RUFF AND A SLUFF. THIS WORKS PARTICULARLY WELL AGAINST A 4-3 TRUMP FIT WHEN ONE DEFENDER HAS FOUR TRUMPS.

(71)   LOOKING FOR FOUR

East-West vulnerable
Dealer North

North
♠ 10 4 3
♡ Q J 3
◇ Q 5
♣ A K J 7 2

East (you)
♠ A 7 6 2
♡ 4 2
◇ 10 8 6
♣ Q 10 8 6

North	East	South	West
1 ♣	Pass	1 ♡	Pass
2 ♡	Pass	4 ♡	All Pass

Opening lead: ♠ J

1. Do you win this trick? If so, what do you return, if not, why not?

LOOKING FOR FOUR   (Solution)

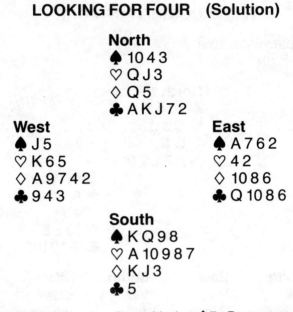

North
♠ 10 4 3
♡ Q J 3
◇ Q 5
♣ A K J 7 2

West
♠ J 5
♡ K 6 5
◇ A 9 7 4 2
♣ 9 4 3

East
♠ A 7 6 2
♡ 4 2
◇ 10 8 6
♣ Q 10 8 6

South
♠ K Q 9 8
♡ A 10 9 8 7
◇ K J 3
♣ 5

Duck the trick, signalling with the ♠7. Partner must have a doubleton. If partner had a singleton declarer would have started with five spades headed by the K Q, unlikely on the bidding.

As you have no side entry, you must retain communications with your partner. You have to hope partner has a trump entry along with his second spade. Upon winning his presumed trump trick, he will return his remaining spade and get a spade ruff. You have to hope he has the ace of diamonds as well. Guess what?

KEY LESSON POINTERS

1. USE THE BIDDING TO GUIDE YOU WHEN PARTNER LEADS A SHORT SUIT TO DETERMINE WHETHER IT IS A SINGLETON OR A DOUBLETON.
2. IF YOU HOLD THE ACE OF THE SUIT PARTNER HAS LED WITH NO OUTSIDE ENTRY, SIGNAL WITH A HIGH-SPOT CARD IF YOU THINK THE LEAD IS FROM A DOUBLETON.
3. PLAYERS WHO LEAD SHORT SUITS FREQUENTLY HAVE A TRUMP ENTRY.
4. WHEN PARTNER LEADS AN HONOR CARD VS. A SUIT CONTRACT, AND YOU CAN SEE THE NEXT LOWER HONOR, THE LEAD MUST BE FROM EITHER A SINGLETON OR A DOUBLTEON.

(72) LUCKY HAND

Both sides vulnerable
Dealer South

                                North
                                ♠ Q 7 6
                                ♡ K Q
                                ◇ 7 6 5
                                ♣ J 10 9 8 7
        West (you)
        ♠ K 5
        ♡ A 10 9
        ◇ J 10 9 8
        ♣ 6 5 3 2

South	**West**	**North**	**East**
1 NT	Pass	2 NT	Pass
3 NT	All Pass		

Opening lead: ◇J

Partner's plays the deuce and declarer wins with the king?

1. What is the likely honor division in diamonds?
2. Can partner have a doubleton diamond?
3. Can partner have a doubleton honor in diamonds?
4. Can partner have the Q42 of diamonds?
   Declarer cashes the ♣ A K dropping partner's doubleton queen and leads the ♡ 6.
5. Which heart do you play? Why?
6. You win the ace and partner drops the ♡4, what do you play now?
7. You play the ♠ K, which holds partner playing the ♠ 2. What do you play now?

LUCKY HAND (Solution)

North
♠ Q 7 6
♡ K Q
◇ 7 6 5
♣ J 10 9 8 7

West
♠ K 5
♡ A 10 9
◇ J 10 9 8
♣ 6 5 3 2

East
♠ A J 10 2
♡ 5 4 3 2
◇ 4 3 2
♣ Q 4

South
♠ 9 8 4 3
♡ J 8 7 6
◇ A K Q
♣ A K

1. Declarer should have the three top honors.
2. Yes. Partner signals attitude, not count, when an honor is led vs. a notrump contract.
3. No. Third hand unblocks with a doubleton honor.
4. Unlikely. Unless partner was very strong in another suit, he would be signalling with Q 4 2.
5. The ♡ A unless declarer is a long lost relative. The heart is declarer's ninth trick.
7. Your other spade. Partners can't always afford to signal with high spot cards. (That is why upside-down attitude signals are better.) In this case if partner signals with an honor in spades he is signalling with the setting trick.

KEY LESSON POINTERS

1. PLAYING UPSIDE DOWN ATTITUDE SIGNALS, A LOW CARD INDICATES STRENGTH AND A HIGH CARD WEAKNESS. THIS METHOD ALSO WORKS VERY WELL WHEN DISCARDING. FOR EXAMPLE, WITH AK1082 YOU CAN DISCARD THE DEUCE TO SHOW STRENGTH AND WITH 872 YOU CAN DISCARD THE EIGHT TO SHOW WEAKNESS. THE RATIONALE IS THAT A PLAYER HOLDING WORTHLESS CARDS IN A SUIT CAN AFFORD TO "WASTE" A HIGH SPOT CARD TO SHOW WEAKNESS, BUT A PLAYER HOLDING STRENGTH IN A SUIT MAY NOT BE ABLE TO AFFORD ONE.

(73) HAVING A VISION

Both sides vulnerable
Dealer South

North
♠ J 10 9
♡ 7 5 3
◇ K J 8
♣ K J 4 3

East (you)
♠ 3 2
♡ Q 10 8 2
◇ A Q 10
♣ 8 6 5 2

South	West	North	East
1 ♠	Pass	2 ♠	All Pass

Opening lead: ♡ K

1. Which heart do you play at trick one? Why?
2. Partner switches to the ◇3 and you capture the ◇J with the ◇Q, declarer playing the ◇7. What do you return at trick three?
3. Partner wins your low heart return and continues with the ◇2. Declarer plays the ◇K, you win and declarer follows with the ◇ 4. What do you play to the next trick?
4. After cashing the ♡Q, everyone following, it is still your lead. Now what?

HAVING A VISION   (Solution)

North
♠ J 10 9
♡ 7 5 3
◇ K J 8
♣ K J 4 3

West
♠ Q 4
♡ A K 4
◇ 9 6 5 3 2
♣ Q 10 7

East
♠ 3 2
♡ Q 10 8 2
◇ A Q 10
♣ 8 6 5 2

South
♠ A K 8 7 6 5
♡ J 9 6
◇ 7 4
♣ A 9

1. Your lowest heart because you want a shift. Partner must work out which suit you want. Your low heart does NOT necessarily ask for a club shift.
2. A low heart to get another diamond play.
3. As the diamond won't cash (partner has shown a five card suit), try to cash the ♡ Q.
4. Play your last heart and hope that partner can take the setting trick by overruffing dummy. The ruff and a sluff can't hurt as declarer is marked with the ♣ A as well as no more diamonds.

   P.S. If partner had a doubleton diamond declarer would be void in clubs. If declarer were void in clubs, partner would be passing with ♡ AKx and ♣ AQ109x. Hardly.

KEY LESSON POINTERS

1. WHEN PARTNER LEADS A HIGH HONOR VS. A SUIT CONTRACT, PLAY LOW IF YOU WANT A SHIFT. PLAY HIGH IF YOU WANT PARTNER TO CONTINUE. THE SIZE OF YOUR LOW CARD DOES NOT INDICATE WHICH SUIT YOU WANT. PARTNER HAS TO WORK IT OUT.
2. WHEN PARTNER LEADS HIGH-LOW DO NOT AUTOMATICALLY ASSUME A DOUBLETON. IT COULD BE A FIVE CARD SUIT. USE THE BIDDING TO GUIDE YOU.
3. WHEN NO TRICKS ARE AVAILABLE IN THE SIDE SUITS, CONSIDER THE POSSIBILITY OF A RUFF AND A SLUFF, PARTICULARLY WHEN IT GIVES PARTNER A CHANCE TO OVERRUFF DUMMY.

(74) INTERESTING

North-South vulnerable
Dealer West

North
♠ 7 4
♡ A 8 4 2
♢ K Q 8
♣ A J 8 7

East (you)
♠ K 3
♡ J 9 7 5
♢ 6 4 3 2
♣ 6 4 2

West	North	East	South
3 ♠	Dbl.	Pass	6 ♣
All Pass			

Opening lead: ♠Q

1. Dummy plays low, which spade do you play? Why?
2. You play low and declarer wins. Declarer draws three rounds of trumps, partner discarding the ♠8 and the ♠6. Assuming partner is giving present count, how many spades did partner begin with?
3. Declarer plays three rounds of diamonds, all following, and exits with the ♠9 to your king. What is declarer's distribution?
4. What do you play at this point?

INTERESTING   (Solution)

North
♠ 7 4
♡ A 8 4 2
◇ K Q 8
♣ A J 8 7

West
♠ Q J 10 8 6 5 2
♡ Q 3
◇ J 10 5
♣ 3

East
♠ K 3
♡ J 9 7 5
◇ 6 4 3 2
♣ 6 4 2

South
♠ A 9
♡ K 10 6
◇ A 9 4
♣ K Q 10 9 5

1. Low. Because if there is a later throw-in play it is better that you, rather than partner, have the lead.
2. Seven. Present count refers to the number of cards remaining at the time of the discard. With an even number of cards remaining (in this case, six) discard a high spot card. With an odd number of cards remaining, discard your lowest card.
3. What you see. You have a count on the minors and partner has shown seven spades.
4. The ♡ 9. This strange looking "surrounding" play insures one heart trick if partner has either the ♡Q or ♡K. If, instead, you lead a low heart and declarer plays low, you do not get a heart trick.

KEY LESSON POINTERS

1. PARTNER'S FIRST DISCARD AFTER AN HONOR LEAD IS USUALLY PRESENT COUNT.
2. THERE IS NO SUBSTITUTE FOR COUNTING THE HAND.
3. WHEN GETTING AROUND TO WHAT APPEARS TO BE THE CRITICAL SUIT, IN THIS CASE, HEARTS, TAKE TIME TO WORK OUT THE POSSIBILITIES.

(75)   SINGLETON LEAD

Both sides vulnerable
Dealer South

North
♠ K Q 9 8 3
♡ Q 10 7
◇ 3 2
♣ J 7 6

West (you)
♠ J
♡ 4 3 2
◇ J 9 8 6 5
♣ A 8 3 2

South	West	North	East
1 ♡	Pass	2 ♡	Pass
4 ♡	All Pass		

Opening lead: ♠ J

Dummy covers and partner wins, declarer following with the ♠ 5. At trick two partner leads the ♣ K, declarer plays the ♣ 4.
1. Which club do you play, why?

SINGLETON LEAD   (Solution)

North
♠ K Q 9 8 3
♡ Q 10 7
◇ 3 2
♣ J 7 6

West
♠ J
♡ 4 3 2
◇ J 9 8 6 5
♣ A 8 5 2

East
♠ A 7 6 4 2
♡ 6
◇ 10 7 4
♣ K Q 10 9

South
♠ 10 5
♡ A K J 9 8 5
◇ A K Q
♣ 5 4

The ♣ 2. You do not want partner to continue clubs, you want a spade ruff. You know you have led a singleton but partner may not. By playing a low club you are saying DON'T lead another club. Partner has to work out whether you want a spade or a diamond.

Once partner sees the low club he will give you a spade ruff. The ace of clubs becomes the setting trick.

KEY LESSON POINTERS

1. WHEN PARTNER LEADS AN HONOR—WHETHER IT BE ON OPENING LEAD OR LATER IN THE HAND—HE IS LOOKING, IN MOST CASES, FOR AN ATTITUDE SIGNAL.
2. THE ATTITUDE SIGNAL IS NOT NECESSARILY GIVEN BY WHAT YOU HAVE IN THE SUIT THAT IS LED, BUT RATHER BY WHAT YOU WANT YOUR PARTNER TO LEAD. IF YOU WANT ANOTHER SUIT, IT DOESN'T MATTER WHAT YOU HAVE IN THE SUIT THAT IS LED—PLAY A LOW CARD. CONVERSELY, IF YOU ARE DEATHLY AFRAID OF A SHIFT, GIVE YOUR PARTER A HIGH CARD EVEN IF YOU HAVE NOTHING OF VALUE IN THE SUIT THAT IS LED. REREAD THIS, IT IS THE KEY TO ATTITUDE SIGNALLING.

(76)   IS IT A GUESS?

East-West vulnerable
Dealer East

North
♠ 2
♡ Q 9 8
◇ Q 7 6 4 3 2
♣ Q 9 8

West (you)
♠ A 8 3
♡ 5 4
◇ K J 8 5
♣ 10 6 5 4

East	South	West	North
1 ♡	1 ♠	1 NT	Pass
2 ♡	3 ♠	All Pass	

Opening lead: ♡ 5

Partner wins the first trick with the ♡10 and continues with the ♡ K and the ♡A. Declarer ruffs the third heart with the ♠ Q.

1. Do you overruff? If you do, what do you return, if you don't what do you discard?
2. Don't overruff. You may be able to promote that ♠ 8 later. For the moment it should be safe to discard the ◇ 8.

    Declarer continues with the ♠ 10 which holds, partner following with the ♠ 3, dummy discarding a diamond, and continues with the ♠ J.
3. Do you win this trick?
4. Win the trick. You don't want to be stuck with the bare ace of trumps. When you win this trick, partner plays the ♠ 9, dummy discarding another diamond. What do you play now?

IS IT A GUESS?   (Solution)

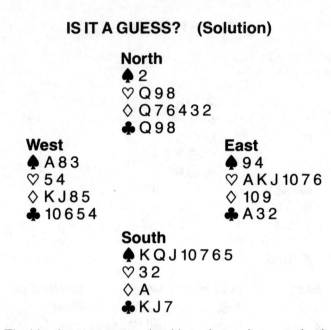

North
♠ 2
♡ Q 9 8
◇ Q 7 6 4 3 2
♣ Q 9 8

West
♠ A 8 3
♡ 5 4
◇ K J 8 5
♣ 10 6 5 4

East
♠ 9 4
♡ A K J 10 7 6
◇ 10 9
♣ A 3 2

South
♠ K Q J 10 7 6 5
♡ 3 2
◇ A
♣ K J 7

The idea is to put partner in with a minor suit ace so that he can play a fourth round of hearts and promote your eight of spades to the setting trick. But which minor?

When you are reduced to what you think must be a guess, consider the cards partner has played thus far. How did he play those hearts? He won the first trick with the ten and then he played the king and the ace. He could have played the ace and then the king, couldn't he?

Maybe he was trying to tell you something. Good partners do that. By playing his lower equals he first was trying to show that his outside strength was in the lower ranking of the two remaining suits. Believe. Return a club. A heart from partner promotes the ♠ 8 to the setting trick.

KEY LESSON POINTERS

1. BE CAREFUL ABOUT OVERRUFFING AN HONOR WITH AN HONOR WHEN DECLARER HAS SHOWN A STRONG TRUMP HOLDING. BY NOT OVERRUFFING YOU MAY PROMOTE A SECONDARY SPOT CARD WITH YET ANOTHER LEAD IN THAT SUIT FROM PARTNER.
2. WHEN PARTNER HAS A CHOICE OF EQUALS, HE SHOULD TRY TO SHOW WHERE HIS OUTSIDE STRENGTH LIES BY THE MANNER IN WHICH HE PLAYS THOSE EQUALS.

(77)   A TRICK IN TIME SAVES NINE

Neither side vulnerable
Dealer South

North
♠ Q J 10 5 4
♡ K Q
◇ 8 7 6
♣ K 8 7

West (you)
♠ 8
♡ J 9 4 3
◇ A K Q J
♣ 9 4 3 2

South	West	North	East
1 NT	Pass	2 ♡*	Pass
2 ♠	Pass	3 NT	Pass
4 ♠	All Pass		

* Transfer bid
Opening lead: ◇ K

You cash the first three diamond tricks, all following.
1. What is the maximum number of high card points partner can have?
2. What do you play to trick four, and what are you hoping for?

A TRICK IN TIME SAVES NINE   (Solution)

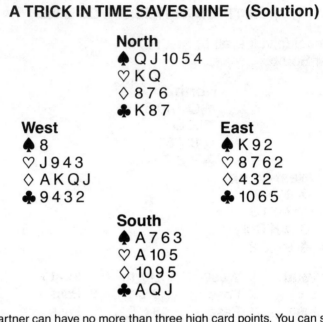

North
♠ Q J 10 5 4
♡ K Q
♢ 8 7 6
♣ K 8 7

West
♠ 8
♡ J 9 4 3
♢ A K Q J
♣ 9 4 3 2

East
♠ K 9 2
♡ 8 7 6 2
♢ 4 3 2
♣ 10 6 5

South
♠ A 7 6 3
♡ A 10 5
♢ 10 9 5
♣ A Q J

1. Partner can have no more than three high card points. You can see 22 between your hand and dummy and declarer must have at least 15.
2. The ♢ J. When there is no hope for a side suit trick (even if partner has the ♣ Q J no trick is coming in that suit because declarer can discard a club from dummy on the ♡ A) look to the trump suit.

   If partner has four spades to the king the hand is always beaten, but if partner has only three spades to the king, including the nine, a fourth diamond will do the trick. If declarer ruffs high in dummy, partner discards and must come to a trump trick. If dummy ruffs low or doesn't ruff at all, partner inserts the ♠ 9, promoting his ♠ K to the setting trick.

KEY LESSON POINTERS

1. ADD YOUR HIGH CARD POINTS TO DUMMY'S HIGH CARD POINTS TO DECLARER'S *MINIMUM* COUNT TO SEE HOW MUCH YOUR PARTNER CAN POSSIBLY HAVE. IF YOU ADD YOUR POINTS TO DUMMY'S POINTS TO DECLARER'S *MAXIMUM* COUNT YOU WILL DISCOVER HOW LITTLE PARTNER CAN POSSIBLY HAVE—VERY DEPRESSING. THE BIDDING WILL FREQUENTLY TELL YOU WHETHER DECLARER IS MAXIMUM OR MINIMUM.
2. WHEN THERE ARE ZERO TRICKS COMING FROM THE SIDE SUITS, CONSIDER GIVING DECLARER A RUFF AND A SLUFF IN THE HOPES OF PROMOTING A TRUMP TRICK.

(78)   LOGIC

Neither side vulnerable
Dealer West

North
♠ A 9 8 7 6 5
♡ 10
◇ 7 6
♣ Q 9 4 2

West (you)
♠ K 10 3
♡ 5 4
◇ A K 10 3 2
♣ A 10 5

West	North	East	South
1 ◇	Pass	2 ◇	4 ♡
All Pass			

Opening lead: ◇K

1. Partner plays the ◇ Q. What does that mean, and what do you play to the second trick?
2. You cash the ◇ A, partner plays the ◇ 8, declarer playing the ◇ 4 and then the ◇ 5. What do you play to the third trick?

LOGIC   (Solution)

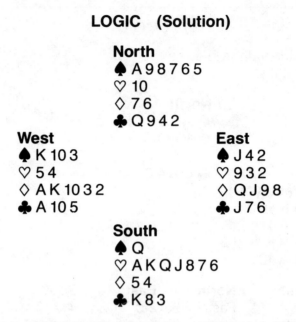

North
♠ A 9 8 7 6 5
♡ 10
♢ 7 6
♣ Q 9 4 2

West
♠ K 10 3
♡ 5 4
♢ A K 10 3 2
♣ A 10 5

East
♠ J 4 2
♡ 9 3 2
♢ Q J 9 8
♣ J 7 6

South
♠ Q
♡ A K Q J 8 7 6
♢ 5 4
♣ K 8 3

1. It means partner has the ♢ J and you can safely underlead if you wish. It is not a command to underlead, it is a suggestion.

    As you do not want your partner to make a possibly damaging club shift, (you do control the spade suit) you should not underlead.
2. After cashing two diamonds the safest exit is a trump: (1) If a finesse in trumps is necessary, declarer always has an entry to take it: (2) you may be killing an entry to the spade suit. Notice that even if you exit with the ♠ K, declarer can set up the suit by means of two ruffs.

    This defense eventually enables you to score two club tricks. If either you or your partner broach the club suit, declarer can hold his losses to one trick in the suit.

KEY LESSON POINTERS

1. THE PLAY OF THE QUEEN UNDER THE LEAD OF THE KING, SIGNI-FIES POSSESSION OF THE JACK (OR A SINGLETON). (IT CAN ALSO BE MADE WITH Qx WHEN THE JACK IS IN THE DUMMY). IT TELLS THE OPENING LEADER IT IS SAFE TO UNDERLEAD IF HE WISHES.
2. WHEN PARTNER PLAYS THE QUEEN UNDER THE KING, DO NOT AUTOMATICALLY UNDERLEAD. IF YOU HAVE NOTHING YOU WANT PARTNER TO PLAY, CONSIDER CASHING THE ACE.
3. WHEN CONTROLLING DUMMY'S LONG SUIT TRY NOT TO BREAK NEW SUITS. LET DECLARER HAVE THE PLEASURE. IF DECLARER CANNOT SET UP THE LONG SUIT, LOSERS IN THE SIDE SUITS WILL EVENTUALLY COME YOUR WAY. PATIENCE.

(79)   SNIFFING IT OUT

Both sides vulnerable
Dealer North

North
♠ A 7 6
♡ J 10 4
◇ A 9 6 3
♣ Q 9 5

West (you)
♠ J 10 9 4
♡ K 9 7
◇ K J 7 5
♣ K 6

North	East	South	West
Pass	Pass	1 ♡	Pass
2 NT	Pass	3 ♣	Pass
4 ♡	All Pass		

Opening lead: ♠ J

Dummy wins, partner plays the ♠ 2 and declarer the ♠ 3.

1. From this one trick, plus the bidding, what is declarer's distribution?
2. At trick two declarer runs the ♡ J to your ♡ K. What do you play to trick three?

SNIFFING IT OUT   (Solution)

North
♠ A 7 6
♡ J 10 4
◇ A 9 6 3
♣ Q 9 5

West
♠ J 10 9 4
♡ K 9 7
◇ K J 7 5
♣ K 6

East
♠ 8 5 2
♡ 8 5
◇ Q 10 8 4 2
♣ A 4 3

South
♠ K Q 3
♡ A Q 6 3 2
◇ —
♣ J 10 8 7 2

1. As declarer should have both remaining spade honors, (partner's ♠ 2 at trick one) he appears to be either 3-5-0-5 or 3-5-1-4.
2. The ♣ K. Counting tricks you determine that declarer has three spade tricks, four hearts and a diamond for eight. If declarer has the ♣ A with the ♣ Q in dummy, there is no hope. Play partner for that one card and shift to the ♣ K at trick three. Down one. Very impressive.

KEY LESSON POINTERS

1. USE PARTNER'S TRICK ONE SIGNAL PLUS THE BIDDING TO WORK OUT DECLARER'S POINT COUNT AND DISTRIBUTION.
2. WHEN DECLARER BIDS TWO SUITS, THE FIRST A MAJOR, ASSUME 5-4 DISTRIBUTION UNTIL YOU LEARN OTHERWISE.
3. LEADING FROM Kx WHEN THE QUEEN IS IN THE DUMMY CAN COST A TRICK IF DECLARER HAS BOTH THE ACE AND THE JACK. HOWEVER, IF PARTNER HAS THE ACE YOU GET AN IMMEDIATE RUFF, AND IF PARTNER HAS THE JACK YOU MIGHT BREAK EVEN. IN ANY CASE, IF PARTNER NEEDS THE ACE TO DEFEAT THE CONTRACT, PLAY HIM FOR IT! BRAVERY, COURAGE, GUTS, DO IT!

(80) PERHAPS

East-West vulnerable
Dealer West

                    North
                    ♠ K Q 9 3 2
                    ♡ Q J 10 7
                    ◇ Q
                    ♣ A J 8
        West (you)
        ♠ 4
        ♡ A K 5
        ◇ K 7 6 5 4
        ♣ K Q 4 2

West	North	East	South
1 ◇	Dlb.	Pass	2 ♠
Pass	4 ♠	All Pass	

Opening lead: ♡ K

Partner plays the ♡ 2, declarer the ♡ 3. What do you play now?

PERHAPS (Solution)

North
♠ K Q 9 3 2
♡ Q J 10 7
◇ Q
♣ A J 8

West
♠ 4
♡ A K 5
◇ K 7 6 5 4
♣ K Q 4 2

East
♠ 10 8
♡ 9 8 4 2
◇ J 9 8 3
♣ 10 7 6

South
♠ A J 7 6 5
♡ 6 3
◇ A 10 2
♣ 9 5 3

A low club. Declarer is marked with both missing aces on the bidding. The only chance is to develop two club tricks before the ace of hearts is knocked out.

Given the clubs you see in the dummy, you must hope that partner has the ♣ 10 and declarer the ♣ 9. If so, when you lead a low club declarer is apt to play low from dummy hoping the club honors are split and that you have the ten. If all this happens, you will defeat the contract one trick. It is your best chance—go for it.

KEY LESSON POINTERS

1. WHEN TWO TRICKS ARE NEEDED IN A SUIT IN WHICH YOU HAVE THE KQ AND DUMMY TO YOUR LEFT HAS THE AJx(x), LEAD LOW AND HOPE PARTNER HAS THE TEN. AT WORST THE PLAY WILL COST AN OVERTRICK—IF YOU HAVE THE HAND FIGURED OUT RIGHT.
2. A JUMP RESPONSE TO A TAKEOUT DOUBLE IS A NON-FORCING BID AND GENERALLY SHOWS 8-10 HIGH CARD POINTS. IT CAN BE MADE ON A FOUR CARD SUIT.

(81)   NOT MANY WILL

Neither side vulnerable
Dealer East

North
♠ Q 9 4
♡ 9 2
◇ K Q J 2
♣ A 10 7 6

West (you)
♠ J 6
♡ 5 4 3
◇ A 7
♣ J 9 8 5 3 2

East	South	West	North
1 ♠	3 ♡*	All Pass	

* Weak
Opening lead: ♠J

Declarer ducks in dummy, partner plays the ♠8 and declarer follows with the ♠5. What do you play to trick two?

NOT MANY WILL   (Solution)

North
♠ Q 9 4
♡ 9 2
◇ K Q J 2
♣ A 10 7 6

West
♠ J 6
♡ 5 4 3
◇ A 7
♣ J 9 8 5 3 2

East
♠ A K 10 8 3
♡ K 8
◇ 10 6 4 3
♣ K 4

South
♠ 7 5 2
♡ A Q J 10 7 6
◇ 9 8 5
♣ Q

The ◇ A. Partner is very likely to have the ♠A K. If that is so, you may be able to make a discard on the third spade. Why not cash the ◇A before leading a second spade? You will discard a diamond on the third spade and ruff the diamond return.

KEY LESSON POINTERS

1. WEAK JUMP OVERCALLS GENERALLY SHOW DECENT SIX CARD SUITS (SOMETIMES SEVEN) WITH LITTLE OUTSIDE STRENGTH.
2. EVERY SO OFTEN YOU CAN ANTICIPATE A DISCARD. IF YOU HAVE Ax IN A SIDE SUIT, CASH YOUR ACE EARLY SO THAT YOU CAN DISCARD YOUR REMAINING CARD AND GET A RUFF. EVERYONE WILL BE SO IMPRESSED.

(82) JUMP PREFERENCE

North-South vulnerable
Dealer South

North
♠ Q J 10 9 2
♡ K 10 4
◇ A 10 9
♣ 3 2

East (you)
♠ K 8 7
♡ A 8 7 6
◇ 7 6
♣ A 8 6 4

South	West	North	East
1 ♡	Pass	1 ♠	Pass
2 ◇	Pass	3 ♡	Pass
4 ♡	All Pass		

Opening lead: ♣ J (Denies a higher honor)

1. Do you win this trick or not?
2. Assume you win the trick, declarer playing the ♣ 5. What do you return at trick two?

JUMP PREFERENCE   (Solution)

North
♠ Q J 10 9 2
♡ K 10 4
◇ A 10 9
♣ 3 2

West
♠ A 6 5 4
♡ 5
◇ 5 4 3 2
♣ J 10 9 7

East
♠ K 8 7
♡ A 8 7 6
◇ 7 6
♣ A 8 6 4

South
♠ 3
♡ Q J 9 3 2
◇ K Q J 8
♣ K Q 5

The ♠ K! Once declarer follows with a low club retaining both honors, he can have at most one spade.

Your plan should be to try to force declarer to ruff spades twice in order to promote your fourth heart to a long suit winner.

In order for your plan to succeed declarer must have a five card trump suit and partner the ♠ A.

Play the ♠ K and continue with a spade. Declarer must ruff. Capture any heart honor with your ace and play another spade. Declarer must ruff again and your fourth heart becomes the setting trick.

KEY LESSON POINTERS

1. USE THE BIDDING PLUS PARTNER'S OPENING LEAD TO WORK OUT DECLARER'S DISTRIBUTION. SOMETIMES YOU CAN DO IT AS EARLY AS TRICK ONE.
2. WHEN TRYING TO PLAY THE FORCING GAME IN A SUIT IN WHICH YOU SEE THE Q J (x) (x) TO YOUR RIGHT, IT MAY BE NECESSARY TO LEAD AN UNSUPPORTED HONOR (IF YOU SUSPECT DECLARER HAS A SINGLETON). THIS PREVENTS DECLARER FROM ESTABLISHING TRICK(S) IN THE SUIT WITHOUT GIVING UP TWO TRICKS.

(83) SPOTS, SPOTS, SPOTS

Neither side vulnerable
Dealer South

> **North**
> ♠ Q J 5 3
> ♡ Q J 9 8
> ◇ Q 8 4
> ♣ 4 3

> **East (you)**
> ♠ 10 8 7 6
> ♡ 7 2
> ◇ 7 6 5 3
> ♣ A J 10

South	West	North	East
2 NT	Pass	3 ♣	Pass
3 ◇	Pass	3 NT	All Pass

Opening lead: ♣ 7

1. Which club do you play?
2. If you didn't play the ace, you have already lost your partner. Assuming you haven't lost your partner, what do you play at trick two? (Declarer having played the deuce of clubs).
3. You return the ♣ J, declarer covers with the ♣ Q and partner wins the trick. Partner returns the ♣ 8 dummy discarding a diamond and declarer following with the ♣ 5. What do you play at trick four?

SPOTS, SPOTS, SPOTS   (Solution)

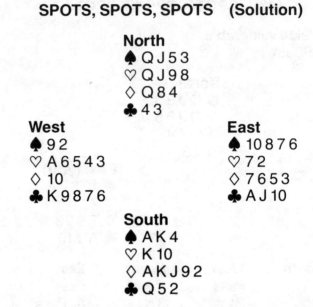

North
- ♠ Q J 5 3
- ♡ Q J 9 8
- ◇ Q 8 4
- ♣ 4 3

West
- ♠ 9 2
- ♡ A 6 5 4 3
- ◇ 10
- ♣ K 9 8 7 6

East
- ♠ 10 8 7 6
- ♡ 7 2
- ◇ 7 6 5 3
- ♣ A J 10

South
- ♠ A K 4
- ♡ K 10
- ◇ A K J 9 2
- ♣ Q 5 2

The ♡ 7. Declarer must have three clubs to the queen—with four to the queen there would be no point in covering. However, holding Qxx the cover works when third hand has AJ10 because the suit is blocked.

Once you come to the conclusion that declarer started with three clubs, partner must have started with five. At the point he returned the third round of clubs, his clubs were precisely 9 8 6. As these clubs are all equals he can tell you which side suit he perfers by means of a suit preference play. The highest club, the nine, indicates spades, the middle club, the eight, hearts, and the lowest club, the six, diamonds. Your partner asked for a heart. Did you read it? If you didn't, they have just chalked up another unmakeable game against you. However, don't worry, it wasn't vulnerable.

KEY LESSON POINTERS

1. DEFENDERS ARE ENTITLED TO MAKE CERTAIN INFERENCES ABOUT DECLARER'S DISTRIBUTION JUDGED FROM THE WAY HE HANDLES CERTAIN CARD COMBINATIONS.
2. WHEN HOLDING EQUAL CARDS, DEFENDERS AT TIMES CAN USE THEIR EQUALS AS SUIT PREFERENCE SIGNALS.
3. IT PAYS TO WATCH THE SPOTS . . . CLOSELY.

(84)   TO COVER OR NOT TO COVER

Both sides vulnerable
Dealer North

North
♠ 6 4
♡ A 7 6
◇ A Q J 7
♣ Q J 9 3

East (you)
♠ 7 5 3
♡ J 10 8
◇ 8 6 4 3
♣ K 8 7

North	East	South	West
1 ◇	Pass	2 NT	Pass
3 NT	All Pass		

Opening lead: ♠ Q

1. Which spade do you play?
2. Declarer wins with the king (who has the ♠ A?) and plays a diamond to dummy's queen, partner playing the ◇ 10. Which diamond do you play?
3. At trick three the ♣ Q is led from dummy. Which club do you play? Why?

TO COVER OR NOT TO COVER   (Solution)

North
♠ 6 4
♡ A 7 6
◇ A Q J 7
♣ Q J 9 3

West
♠ Q J 10 9 2
♡ Q 5 3 2
◇ 10 9
♣ A 6

East
♠ 7 5 3
♡ J 10 8
◇ 8 6 4 3
♣ K 8 7

South
♠ A K 8
♡ K 9 4
◇ K 5 2
♣ 10 5 4 2

1. The ♠ 3 attitude, to deny a spade honor.
2. You can't be sure who has the ♠ A. Declarer is more likely to hold it, but it is possible that your partner has led from an A Q J combination. The ◇ 6. Second high from four small if you wish to give count.
3. The ♣ K. Although it is not 100% clear (it could be wrong if declarer has no spade stopper and something like ♣ Axx), the percentage play is to assume declarer has the ♠ A and partner the ♣ A. If that is the case, you, not partner, must win the first club in order to drive out declarer's remaining spade stopper. When partner later gets the lead with the ♣ A his spades will be established.

    The defense would have been easier had South held up on the first spade. If South wins the second spade, the position is clear and partner must be played for the ♣ A in order to break the contract.

KEY LESSON POINTERS

*1. WHEN PARTNER LEADS THE QUEEN VS. NO TRUMP AND THERE ARE NO HONORS IN DUMMY, GIVE ATTITUDE, NOT COUNT.
2. WHEN GIVING COUNT WITH FOUR SMALL PLAY THE SECOND HIGHEST.
3. WHEN TRYING TO ESTABLISH PARTNER'S SUIT AT NO TRUMP, IT IS IMPORTANT THAT YOU USE YOUR ENTRY FIRST, RETAINING PARTNER'S ENTRY FOR A LATER DATE WHEN HIS SUIT IS ESTABLISHED.
    * BUT IF DUMMY HAS AN HONOR AND IT IS NOT PLAYED, GIVE COUNT.

(85) UNBLOCK

East-West vulnerable
Dealer North

                              North
                              ♠ J 10 7 6 4
                              ♡ 7 4 3
                              ◇ A J 10
                              ♣ A 10
        West (you)
        ♠ A
        ♡ K Q J 9 5 2
        ◇ 9 4 3
        ♣ K 9 3

North	**East**	**South**	**West**
Pass	Pass	1 ♠	2 ♡
4 ♠	All Pass		

Opening lead: ♡ K

   Partner overtakes and returns a heart, declarer following
to both rounds. What do you play to trick three?

UNBLOCK   (Solution)

North
♠ J 10 7 6 4
♡ 7 4 3
◇ A J 10
♣ A 10

West
♠ A
♡ K Q J 9 5 2
◇ 9 4 3
♣ K 9 3

East
♠ 3 2
♡ A 8
◇ 8 7 6 5 2
♣ J 8 7 6

South
♠ K Q 9 8 5
♡ 10 6
◇ K Q
♣ Q 5 4 2

The ♠ A. If partner has the ♣ Q and declarer four diamonds, it is right to shift to a club while you still have the trump ace. Otherwise, declarer will be able to discard dummy's ♣ 10 on the fourth diamond.

However, this line of defense requires a parlay.

(1) the ♣ Q in partner's hand: (2) four diamonds in declarer's hand. Better to hope that declarer has an eventual club loser. For this you need to find partner with the ♣ J.

In order to get a club trick, and not be forced to lead away from your ♣ K, cash the ♠ A at trick three and exit with a high heart. Eventually you get a club trick.

If you carelessly continue with a high heart, declarer ruffs, strips the diamonds and leads a spade. Now you have to either break the club suit or give declarer the dreaded ruff and a sluff.

KEY LESSON POINTERS

1. ALWAYS TRY TO DREAM UP A DEFENSE THAT WILL DEFEAT THE CONTRACT.
2. IF TWO DREAMS COME TO MIND, PLAY FOR THE ONE THAT REQUIRES THE LEAST FROM PARTNER.
3. DEFENSES THAT REQUIRE PARLAYS (TWO OR MORE GOOD THINGS TO HAPPEN) SHOULD ONLY BE LAST RESORT MEASURES.
4. THE SINGLETON ACE OF TRUMPS CAN BE A LIABILITY AS IT MAY OPEN YOU UP TO AN EVENTUAL ENDPLAY IF NOT CASHED EARLY.
5. ALTHOUGH IT WASN'T TRUE ON THIS DEAL, BE ON THE LOOKOUT FOR LIGHT THIRD HAND OPENINGS, PARTICULARLY AT FAVORABLE VULNERABILITY.

(86)   100 HONORS

East-West vulnerable
Dealer South

North
♠ 8 2
♡ A Q J 10 5
◇ 7 6 4
♣ Q J 8

East (you)
♠ A K 7 6
♡ 9 6 4 3 2
◇ 10 5
♣ 4 3

South	West	North	East
1 NT	Pass	2 ◇ *	Pass
2 ♡	Pass	3 NT	All Pass

* Transfer
Opening lead: ◇ 3

Your ten fetches declarer's king.
1. How many diamonds does partner have?
2. How many hearts?
3. At trick three declarer leads a low club to partner's ace, which club do you play?
4. At trick four partner leads the ♠ 3 which you win, declarer playing the ♠ 9. What do you return at trick five?

100 HONORS (Solution)

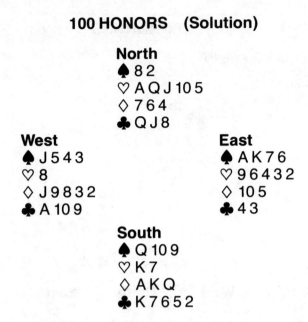

North
- ♠ 8 2
- ♡ A Q J 10 5
- ♢ 7 6 4
- ♣ Q J 8

West
- ♠ J 5 4 3
- ♡ 8
- ♢ J 9 8 3 2
- ♣ A 10 9

East
- ♠ A K 7 6
- ♡ 9 6 4 3 2
- ♢ 10 5
- ♣ 4 3

South
- ♠ Q 10 9
- ♡ K 7
- ♢ A K Q
- ♣ K 7 6 5 2

1. Either four or five depending upon who has the ♢ 2.
2. Probably a doubleton. With three hearts, South might have preferred hearts knowing partner has a five card suit.
3. The ♣ 4. No reason not to give count.
4. A low spade. Had partner wanted a diamond return he would have shifted to a high spade. As partner can have no more than four spades, declarer must have three. If those spades are specifically Q 10 9, you can put declarer to an ugly guess by returning a low spade.

    Seeing this all in advance, you might win the first spade lead with the ace, giving declarer the impression that partner has the ♠ K.

KEY LESSON POINTERS

1. WHEN DUMMY HAS A LONG SUIT MISSING THE ACE OR KING, AND THE DECLARER DOESN'T ATTACK THE SUIT AT ONCE, CHANCES ARE DECLARER HAS THE MISSING HONOR.
2. THE SPADE COMBINATION IN THIS PROBLEM IS WORTH AN-OTHER LOOK. EAST CANNOT AFFORD TO LEAD LOW THE SEC-OND TIME IF DECLARER CAN HAVE A DOUBLETON. HE MAY HAVE Qx! HOWEVER, GIVEN THAT DECLARER HAS MORE THAN A DOUBLETON, IT IS RIGHT FOR EAST TO RETURN LOW AND PUT DECLARER TO A POSSIBLE GUESS.

(87)   DIAMONDS OVER DIAMONDS

East-West vulnerable
Dealer South

North
♠ A K Q
♡ Q 6 5
◇ Q 10 8 7 2
♣ 4 3

East (you)
♠ J 5
♡ A 4 3
◇ K J 9 6 5
♣ A 9 7

South	West	North	East
1 ♡	Pass	2 ◇	Pass
2 ♡	Pass	4 ♡	All Pass

Opening lead: ♣ 2

1. If you had to guess declarer's distribution, what would you guess?
2. After winning the ♣ A, what do you return at trick two?

DIAMONDS OVER DIAMONDS   (Solution)

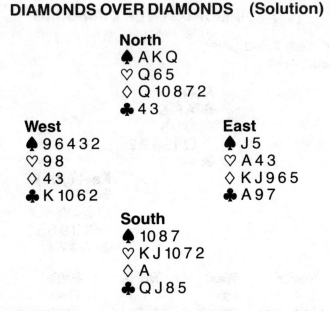

North
♠ A K Q
♡ Q 6 5
◇ Q 10 8 7 2
♣ 4 3

West
♠ 9 6 4 3 2
♡ 9 8
◇ 4 3
♣ K 10 6 2

East
♠ J 5
♡ A 4 3
◇ K J 9 6 5
♣ A 9 7

South
♠ 10 8 7
♡ K J 10 7 2
◇ A
♣ Q J 8 5

Declarer is known to have at least five hearts and four clubs judging from partner's lead. With three diamonds missing, it is likely that if partner had the singleton he would have led it, so it is declarer who has it. Therefore, declarer is either 2-6-1-4 or 3-5-1-4.

Your best return at trick two is a low heart playing partner for the ♣ K as well as a second heart. This is going to be an impossible hand to defeat if declarer has six hearts as he is marked with the ◇ A for his opening bid.

With the low heart return, declarer must lose three clubs and a heart.

KEY LESSON POINTERS

1. WHEN YOU CAN SEE TEN CARDS OF A SUIT BETWEEN YOUR HAND AND DUMMY, ASSUME DECLARER HAS THE SINGLETON IF THE SUIT IS NOT LED.
2. WHEN A PLAYER CAN HAVE EITHER A FIVE OR A SIX CARD TRUMP SUIT ON THE BIDDING, ASSUME FIVE IF YOU CANNOT DEFEAT THE HAND OTHERWISE.
3. WHEN DECLARER REBIDS HIS ORIGINAL SUIT, PLAY HIM FOR A SIX CARD SUIT IF HE HAS SKIPPED OVER A NUMBER OF SUITS, INCLUDING NO TRUMP, TO REBID HIS SUIT. IF HE HAS NOT SKIPPED OVER ANY SUITS, TEND TO PLAY HIM FOR A FIVE CARD SUIT. FOR EXAMPLE, 1 ♡-1 ♠, 2♡ SHOWS A SIX CARD SUIT (HAVING SKIPPED OVER 1 NT, 2 ♣ and 2 ◇) BUT 1 ♡-2 ◇, 2♡ IS LIKELY TO BE A FIVE CARD SUIT.

(88) THE MAN MUST KNOW SOMETHING

Both vulnerable
Dealer South

North
♠ Q 7 5
♡ K 8 7
♢ A Q J 9 4
♣ 4 2

East (you)
♠ 10 3
♡ 3 2
♢ K 10 8 3 2
♣ 10 9 7 3

South	West	North	East
1 ♡	1 ♠	2 ♢	Pass
2 ♡	3 ♣	3 ♡	All Pass

Opening lead: ♠ K

You play the ♠ 10 and partner continues with the ♠ A and the ♠ J. You ruff the third spade and declarer follows.
1. What do you think partner's distribution is?
2. What do you return at trick four?

THE MAN MUST KNOW SOMETHING   (Solution)

North
♠ Q 7 5
♡ K 8 7
◇ A Q J 9 4
♣ 4 2

West
♠ A K J 9 4
♡ J 10 5
◇ —
♣ Q J 8 6 5

East
♠ 10 3
♡ 3 2
◇ K 10 8 3 2
♣ 10 9 7 3

South
♠ 8 6 2
♡ A Q 9 6 3
◇ 7 6 5
♣ A K

Partner is marked with five spades and as his return of the ♠ J screams for a diamond, he must be void.

Therefore, partner has either 5-3-0-5 or 5-2-0-6. With the second distribution he would have bid clubs first, so he must have what you see.

This one is a bit tricky. You know your partner is void in diamonds and you know that if you give him a ruff you still retain the setting trick with the ◇ K. But does he know? No.

What you must prevent your partner from doing is leading a fourth spade in the hopes that perhaps you have a highish heart and can uppercut declarer. Therefore, even though you don't want a club return, it can't cost (any club loser will go on a diamond anyway), and it does insure a set. Your proper return is the ◇ 2 asking for a club return after partner ruffs. You get your club switch and you also make the king of diamonds for down one. Had you returned a high diamond to stop a club switch, partner might have played you for something like:

♠ 10x ♡ Qx ◇ 10xxxxx ♣ xxx and returned a spade. Now declarer makes the unmakeable contract.

KEY LESSON POINTERS

1. WHEN PARTNER GIVES YOU A RUFF, WATCH THE CARD HE PLAYS. IF HE HAD A CHOICE OF CARDS, HIS RETURN IS A SUIT PREFERENCE SIGNAL.
2. WHEN GIVING PARTNER A RUFF, BE EQUALLY CAREFUL. THE CARD YOU PLAY IS A SUIT PREFERENCE RETURN SIGNAL.
3. IN THE EXCEPTIONAL CASE (YOU RETAIN A SURE TRICK IN THE SUIT YOU ARE LEADING FOR PARTNER TO RUFF), MAKE SURE YOUR PARTNER DOESN'T COST YOU THAT TRICK BY PERHAPS GIVING DECLARER A RUFF AND A SLUFF IN SEARCH OF AN UPPERCUT. GOOD PARTNERS THINK OF THINGS LIKE THAT.

(89)   TRAPPED KING

North-South vulnerable
Dealer South

> **North**
> ♠ K 9 6
> ♡ A 9 3 2
> ◇ 10 5 2
> ♣ 10 5 2

> **East (you)**
> ♠ A 7 3
> ♡ 4
> ◇ 8 6 4 3
> ♣ Q 8 6 4 3

South	West	North	East
1 ♡	2 ♠*	Pass	4 ♠
5 ◇	Pass	5 ♡	All Pass

* Weak
Opening lead: ♠ Q

1. Dummy plays low, which spade do you play?

TRAPPED KING   (Solution)

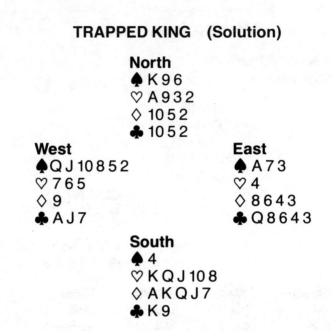

North
♠ K 9 6
♡ A 9 3 2
◇ 10 5 2
♣ 10 5 2

West
♠ Q J 10 8 5 2
♡ 7 6 5
◇ 9
♣ A J 7

East
♠ A 7 3
♡ 4
◇ 8 6 4 3
♣ Q 8 6 4 3

South
♠ 4
♡ K Q J 10 8
◇ A K Q J 7
♣ K 9

1. The ♠ A. If this were a normal count situation, you would play the ♠ 3 as partner will know that you have the ♠ A when the queen holds. However, this is not a normal count situation. Declarer is marked with a two-suiter and there is a danger of losing a club winner with passive defense. (Declarer draws trumps and discards two clubs from dummy on good diamonds, eventually losing one trick in each black suit.) Your play is to win the ♠ A and immediately shift to a low club. It's not the ♠ K that's trapped, it's the ♣ K. Did the title fool you? Ho, Ho, Ho.

KEY LESSON POINTERS

1. WHEN PARTNER LEADS THE QUEEN, DUMMY HAS THE KING, AND YOU, THIRD HAND, HAVE THE ACE, GIVE COUNT IF DUMMY PLAYS LOW UNLESS YOU ARE SURE DECLARER HAS A SINGLETON AND YOU MUST HAVE THE LEAD AT ONCE.
2. WHEN DEFENDING AGAINST A TWO—SUITER, THE KEY TO MANY A DEFENSE IS WHETHER OR NOT DECLARER CAN DRAW TRUMPS AND STILL REMAIN WITH AT LEAST ONE TRUMP IN DUMMY. IF HE CAN, THEN THERE IS A DANGER THAT HE CAN USE HIS SECOND SUIT TO DISCARD A LOSER(S) FROM DUMMY AND LATER RUFF IN DUMMY. IF THAT DANGER DOES NOT EXIST, THERE IS NO NEED FOR THE DEFENDERS TO SCURRY AROUND LOOKING FOR TRICKS BY ATTACKING NEW SUITS. THE TRICKS WILL COME—THEY CANNOT DISAPPEAR.

(90)   MICHAELS' CUE

Neither side vulnerable
Dealer South

North
♠ 4 2
♡ 9 2
◇ A K 9 7 6 2
♣ K J 6

East (you)
♠ A K 3
♡ 8 6 3
◇ Q 10 5 3
♣ 5 4 3

South	West	North	East
1 ♣	2 ♣*	2 ◇	2 ♠
3 ♣	Pass	5 ♣	All Pass

* Majors
Opening lead: ♠Q

1. Which spade do you play at trick one?
2. Assuming you have won the trick with the ♠K, what do you play at trick two?
3. Assuming you have cashed the ♠A and partner has played the ♠9, indicating an original holding of an odd number of spades, what do you play at trick three?

MICHAELS' CUE   (Solution)

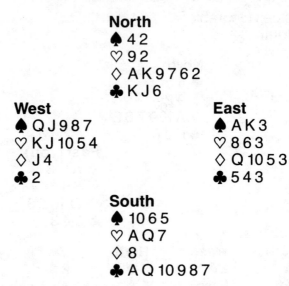

North
- ♠ 4 2
- ♡ 9 2
- ◇ A K 9 7 6 2
- ♣ K J 6

West
- ♠ Q J 9 8 7
- ♡ K J 10 5 4
- ◇ J 4
- ♣ 2

East
- ♠ A K 3
- ♡ 8 6 3
- ◇ Q 10 5 3
- ♣ 5 4 3

South
- ♠ 10 6 5
- ♡ A Q 7
- ◇ 8
- ♣ A Q 10 9 8 7

Your remaining spade. Once you force dummy to trump a spade, you kill the diamond suit. Declarer can no longer set up the diamond suit. Once the diamonds are established, declarer cannot end up in the dummy after drawing trumps. Your three little trumps prevent this. Once the diamond suit has been silenced you will get whatever heart trick(s) you have coming.

Had you only two trumps, it would be necessary to shift to a heart after cashing two spades because the diamond suit would be easily establishable.

KEY LESSON POINTERS

1. PARTNER'S SECOND PLAY IN A SUIT IN WHICH HE HAS ORIGINALLY LED AN HONOR IS NORMALLY PRESENT COUNT.
   FOR EXAMPLE: (A) Q J 10 9 4 2 (YOU REMAIN WITH J 10 9 4 2)
                        (B) Q J 10 7 3 (YOU REMAIN WITH J 10 7 3)
   ASSUME THE ♠Q IS LED AND OVERTAKEN AND THE ♠A CASHED. WITH (A) THE DEUCE IS PLAYED TO SHOW AN ODD NUMBER OF CARDS REMAINING. WITH (B) THE SEVEN IS PLAYED TO SHOW AN EVEN NUMBER OF CARDS REMAINING.
2. WHEN THREATENED WITH A LONG SUIT THAT CAN BE ESTABLISHED BY RUFFING, THE BEST DEFENSE IS TO KILL THE ENTRY TO THAT SUIT. SOMETIMES THE ONLY ENTRY IS IN THE TRUMP SUIT. BY FORCING THE DUMMY TO RUFF YOU CAN EFFECTIVELY KILL THE SUIT—PROVIDING AT LEAST ONE DEFENDER NOW REMAINS WITH A LONGER TRUMP HOLDING THAN THE DUMMY.

(91)   LUCKY YOU

Both sides vulnerable
Dealer East

North
♠ 10 9 8
♡ Q 10 7 5
◇ 8 4
♣ A K Q 10

East
♠ A Q 6 5 4 3
♡ A 4 2
◇ Q J 10
♣ 9

East	South	West	North
1 ♠	1 NT*	Pass	2 ♠**
Pass	3 ♡	Pass	4 ♡
All Pass			

* 16-18
** Stayman
Opening lead: ♠ 2

You win the ♠ A and declarer plays the ♠ J. What do you play at trick two?

LUCKY YOU   (Solution)

North
♠ 10 9 8
♡ Q 10 7 5
◊ 8 4
♣ A K Q 10

West
♠ 2
♡ 6 3
◊ 7 6 5 3 2
♣ 8 7 5 4 3

East
♠ A Q 6 5 4 3
♡ A 4 2
◊ Q J 10
♣ 9

South
♠ K J 7
♡ K J 9 8
◊ A K 9
♣ J 6 2

The ♣ 9. Partner has led an obvious singleton and you can, of course, give him an immediate ruff. But where will the setting trick come from? If you count points you discover that partner must be pointless! Between you and the dummy there are 24 points and declarer must have at least 16. Furthermore, partner only has two trumps so you can only give him one ruff. Why not go for a ruff yourself? Switch to your singleton club. Win the first trump play, give partner a spade ruff (lead your lowest spade in case partner is sleeping) and get a club ruff in return. You play so intelligently.

KEY LESSON POINTERS

1. THE ACE OF TRUMPS IS A BEAUTIFUL CARD—DON'T SQUANDER IT. WHEN PARTNER LEADS AN OBVIOUS SINGLETON, CONSIDER RETURNING YOUR OWN SHORT SUIT BEFORE GIVING PARTNER A RUFF. THAT WAY, WHEN YOU DO GIVE PARTNER A RUFF, YOU WILL BE ABLE TO RUFF SOMETHING AS WELL.
2. NINE TIMES OUT OF TEN THE BIDDING TELLS YOU HOW MANY TRUMPS PARTNER HAS. WHEN IT COMES TO GIVING PARTNER RUFFS, THIS INFORMATION COMES IN MIGHTY HANDY. FOR EXAMPLE, ON THIS HAND YOU KNOW PARTNER HAS TWO TRUMPS AND THEREFORE CAN RUFF ONLY ONCE.
3. DON'T GET LAZY. ADD YOUR POINTS TO DUMMY'S AND THE TOTAL TO DECLARER'S APPROXIMATE COUNT TO ZERO IN ON PARTNER'S STRENGTH.

(92) LOWLY PART SCORE

East-West vulnerable
Dealer South

North
♠ 8 7 4 3 2
♡ J 4
◇ A 10 5
♣ Q 8 6

East (you)
♠ J 10 9 6 5
♡ A 9
◇ J 9 8 2
♣ A J

South	West	North	East
1♡	Pass	1♠	Pass
2♡	All Pass		

Opening lead: ♠Q

1. Which spade do you play?
2. Declarer wins the opening lead with the ♠A, and leads a low heart to the jack, partner playing the six. You win the ace. What do you return.
3. You return a low spade, partner ruffs with the ♡5 and returns the ♣3, dummy playing low. Which club do you play?
4. You play the ace. What do you return?

LOWLY PART SCORE   (Solution)

North
♠ 8 7 4 3 2
♡ J 4
◇ A 10 6
♣ Q 8 6

West
♠ Q
♡ 7 6 5
◇ K 7 4 3
♣ K 9 4 3 2

East
♠ J 10 9 6 5
♡ A 9
◇ J 9 8 2
♣ A J

South
♠ A K
♡ K Q 10 8 3 2
◇ Q 6
♣ 10 7 5

1. The ♠ 5, your lowest spade to indicate where your outside strength lies when partner leads a known singleton.
2. ♠ 6. Your lowest remaining spade, once again showing ♣ strength.
3. The ♣ A. Partner should have a high honor for his low club lead plus there is a danger of an impending endplay on partner if the club suit isn't cleared quickly.
4. The ♣ J. Go a ruff of your own rather than try and promote something unpromotable for partner. Declarer is marked with six hearts to the K Q so no promotion is possible. After you get your club ruff you can exit with a spade and wait for your diamond trick—the setting trick.

KEY LESSON POINTERS

1. WHEN PARTNER LEADS AN OBVIOUS SINGLETON, GIVE SUIT PREFERENCE AT TRICK ONE.
2. WHEN LOOKING FOR A RUFF BE SURE TO PLAY HIGH-LOW IN THE TRUMP SUIT TO SHOW THREE TRUMPS. OTHERWISE PARTNER WILL ASSUME YOU DON'T HAVE A THIRD TRUMP.

(93)   YOUR PLAY

Neither side vulnerable
Dealer South

North
♠ 7 6 3
♡ A J 4
◇ K Q J 10
♣ K 6 3

East (you)
♠ Q 10 4
♡ 10 3 2
◇ 8 7 4 2
♣ A 7 5

South	West	North	East
Pass	Pass	1 ◇	Pass
1 ♡	Pass	1 NT	Pass
2 NT	Pass	3 ♡	Pass
4 ♡	All Pass		

Opening lead: ♣ J

1. How many points do you think declarer has?
2. How many hearts?
3. Can the hand be defeated if declarer has the ◇A?
4. What card do you play to trick one? Why?

YOUR PLAY   (Solution)

North
♠ 7 6 3
♡ A J 4
◇ K Q J 10
♣ K 6 3

West
♠ K J 5 2
♡ 9 8
◇ A 6 5
♣ J 10 9 8

East
♠ Q 10 4
♡ 10 3 2
◇ 8 7 4 2
♣ A 7 5

South
♠ A 9 8
♡ K Q 7 6 5
◇ 9 3
♣ Q 4 2

1. 10 or 11 high card points. As declarer is marked with a five card heart suit, he would have opened the bidding had he 12 high card points.
2. Five. Partner has shown 3 card support, and the assumption is that South would not go to game in hearts knowing he would be playing a 4-3 fit.
3. Yes. If partner has the ♠ AJxx. Win the club and shift to a spade honor.
4. The ♣ A. True, by winning the ♣ A you are giving declarer two club tricks, but in return you may be scoring at least two spade tricks to go along with partner's ◇ A. If you duck the club and declarer has the ♠A (see diagram) you will not score a single spade trick. Furthermore, if declarer has the ◇A and partner the ♠ AJxx, you must win the first club and shift to a spade honor. The key to the defense is that you don't have time to duck the club given the threat of the diamond suit.

KEY LESSON POINTERS

1. BEFORE PLAYING TO THE FIRST TRICK TRY TO WORK OUT DECLARER'S POINT COUNT AND DISTRIBUTION. TRICK TWO MAY BE TOO LATE!
2. AND DON'T FORGET TO COUNT DECLARER'S TRICKS!
3. PAY ATTENTION TO ORIGINAL PASSES. IF DECLARER IS A PASSED HAND HIS POINT COUNT IS SEVERELY LIMITED.

(94) PLANS

Both sides vulnerable
Dealer South

North
♠ A K 5
♡ A Q 3
◇ 7 6 3
♣ 9 8 7 6

East (you)
♠ Q 9 8 7 4 3
♡ J 10 8 5
◇ K Q 8
♣ —

South	West	North	East
Pass	1 ♣	Dbl.	1 ♠
2 ◇	3 ♣	Pass	Pass
3 ◇	All Pass		

Opening lead: ♣ Q*

    * You conventionally lead the queen from A K Q as well as top of a sequence.

1. Do you ruff, or do you discard? If you discard, what do you discard?
2. You discard a ♡. Partner continues with the ♣ K, (indicating an original even number of clubs). What do you discard this time?

PLANS   (Solution)

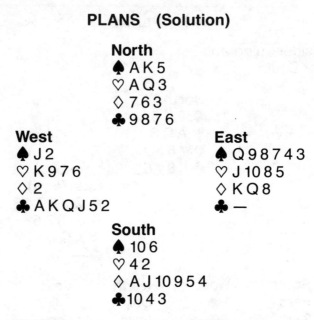

North
♠ A K 5
♡ A Q 3
◇ 7 6 3
♣ 9 8 7 6

West
♠ J 2
♡ K 9 7 6
◇ 2
♣ A K Q J 5 2

East
♠ Q 9 8 7 4 3
♡ J 10 8 5
◇ K Q 8
♣ —

South
♠ 10 6
♡ 4 2
◇ A J 10 9 5 4
♣ 10 4 3

Another heart, and continue discarding hearts on each of partner's clubs. You might get a chance to discard as many as four hearts if partner started with a six card club suit headed by either the A K Q J or the A K Q 10.

By discarding four hearts you might convince the declarer that it is not in his own best interest to take the percentage play in diamonds (two finesses) for fear of an impending heart ruff.

If, after ruffing the fourth club, declarer plunks down the ◇ A, you have talked him into a one trick set. If you do not discard hearts, he will not fear taking the double diamond finesse.

KEY LESSON POINTERS

1. YOU AND YOUR FAVORITE PARTNER MIGHT CONSIDER ADOPTING THE LEAD OF THE QUEEN VS. SUIT CONTRACTS FROM THE A K Q WHEN THE SUIT HAS BEEN BID STRONGLY OR THE OPENING LEADER HAS SHOWN A STRONG HAND. THIRD HAND IS REQUIRED TO GIVE COUNT. THE OPENING LEADER CONTINUES WITH THE KING TO SHOW AN EVEN NUMBER OF CARDS IN THE SUIT, WITH THE ACE TO SHOW AN ODD NUMBER.
2. WHEN YOU ARE AFRAID THAT DECLARER WILL ADOPT THE WINNING LINE OF PLAY, THE IDEA IS TO TALK·HIM OUT OF IT ONE WAY OR THE OTHER. MAKING HIM FEAR AN IMPENDING RUFF IS ONE WAY.

(95) REALLY?

Both sides vulnerable
Dealer North

North
♠ A K 10
♡ 8 4
◇ Q 7 6 3
♣ K 10 6 5

East (you)
♠ Q 9 7 3 2
♡ J 7 5 3
◇ A 10 9 8
♣ —

North	East	South	West
1 ◇	Pass	1 ♡	Pass
1 NT	Pass	4 ♡	All Pass

Opening lead: ♣ A

You discard the ♠ 7 and partner continues with the ♣ 9 which you ruff, declarer playing the ♣ Q.
What do you return at trick three?

REALLY? (Solution)

North
♠ A K 10
♡ 8 4
◇ Q 7 6 3
♣ K 10 6 5

West
♠ J 8 6 5
♡ Q
◇ J 2
♣ A J 9 8 4 3

East
♠ Q 9 7 3 2
♡ J 7 5 3
◇ A 10 9 8
♣ —

South
♠ 4
♡ A K 10 9 6 2
◇ K 5 4
♣ Q 7 2

The ♠ 3. Partner has asked for spade return with his high club play. Clearly he does not have the ◇K. Why not believe?

In fact, you get a bonus with your return. You have removed a dummy entry prematurely. Declarer can no longer cash one high trump and reenter to finesse your ♡J even if he has seen your hand!

KEY LESSON POINTERS

1. WHEN PARTNER GIVES YOU A RUFF HE ALSO TELLS YOU WHAT SUIT HE WANTS RETURNED. UNLESS YOU HAVE A COMPELLING REASON TO GO AGAINST HIS WISHES—DON'T.
2. WHEN PLAYING WITH DECIDEDLY A STRONGER PLAYER THAN YOURSELF, (A RARITY) TEND TO FOLLOW PARTNER'S LINE OF DEFENSE. WHEN PLAYING WITH A DECIDEDLY WEAKER PLAYER, TEND TO TAKE CHARGE OF THE DEFENSE.
3. WHEN RESPONDER JUMPS TO GAME IN HIS OWN SUIT AFTER OPENER HAS REBID ONE NOTRUMP, PLAY HIM FOR A SIX CARD SUIT PLUS OPENING OR NEAR OPENING BID VALUES.

(96)   NICE DUMMY TO FIND

East-West vulnerable
Dealer West

North
♠ 8 7 6 5
♡ 3
♢ A Q J 10 8 7
♣ K 6

East (you)
♠ J 4
♡ A 5
♢ 6 5 4 3
♣ A 10 9 8 7

West	North	East	South
3 ♡	Pass	4 ♡	4 ♠
All Pass			

Opening lead: ♡ Q

You win the ♡ A.
1. What do you play to trick two?
2. You cash the ♣ A, declarer playing the ♣ J, and partner the ♣ 4. What do you play to trick three?

NICE DUMMY TO FIND   (Solution)

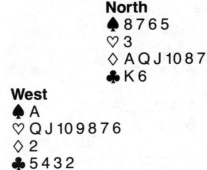

North
♠ 8 7 6 5
♡ 3
♢ A Q J 10 8 7
♣ K 6

West
♠ A
♡ Q J 10 9 8 7 6
♢ 2
♣ 5 4 3 2

East
♠ J 4
♡ A 5
♢ 6 5 4 3
♣ A 10 9 8 7

South
♠ K Q 10 9 3 2
♡ K 4 2
♢ K 9
♣ Q J

The ♡ 5. You must discount the possibility that partner has a diamond void. Had he a diamond void he
would not have led a normal looking heart. He would
have led either an abnormally high or low spot card to
alert you.

Once you need not worry about the diamond void
possibility, the best chance to defeat the contract is to
hope partner has the ♠ A. If so, a heart return will do the
trick. Partner wins the ♠ A and returns a third heart allowing you to overruff dummy for the fourth defensive
trick.

KEY LESSON POINTERS

1. WHEN A PREEMPTIVE BIDDER HAS A SIDE VOID
   HE SHOULD NOT MAKE A NORMAL LOOKING
   OPENING LEAD IN HIS SUIT. WITH A LOWER
   RANKING VOID AN ABNORMALLY LOW SPOT
   CARD IS LED, VICE VERSA WITH A HIGHER
   RANKING VOID.
2. THERE IS NO LAW THAT SAYS PARTNER CAN'T
   HOLD THE TRUMP ACE. IF YOU NEED THAT
   CARD IN PARTNER'S HAND TO DEFEAT THE
   CONTRACT, PLAY HIM FOR IT.

(97) UPON REFLECTION

East-West vulnerable
Dealer North

North
♠ Q J 9
♡ J 9 4 3
◇ K J 6 5
♣ Q J

West (you)
♠ A 8 7 6
♡ Q 10 2
◇ 10 9 8
♣ A 6 2

North	East	South	West
Pass	Pass	1 ♡	Pass
3 ♡	All Pass		

Opening lead: ◇ 10

Declarer wins with the ◇A, plays off the ♡A K, partner following, continues with the ◇Q and a third diamond to dummy, partner following, and plays a fourth diamond. Partner discards the ♠ 5, and declarer the ♠ 2.

1. Do you ruff? If so, what do you return? If you do not ruff, what do you discard?
2. You discard a high spade and the ♣ Q is led from dummy, partner playing the ♣ 8 and declarer the ♣ 4. Do you win this trick? If so, what do you return?
3. You cash the ♡Q and partner discards the ♠ 10. Now what?

UPON REFLECTION   (Solution)

North
♠ Q J 9
♡ J 9 4 3
◇ K J 6 5
♣ Q J

West
♠ A 8 7 6
♡ Q 10 2
◇ 10 9 8
♣ A 6 2

East
♠ K 10 5 3
♡ 8 7
◇ 7 4 3
♣ K 8 7 5

South
♠ 4 2
♡ A K 6 5
◇ A Q 2
♣ 10 9 4 3

It would be an error to ruff the fourth diamond. That would leave declarer with two trumps. He would be able to ruff two spades in his own hand, losing one spade trick along with the ♣ A K. Better to gain the lead with one of your black aces and draw two trumps with the ♡ Q.

Win the ♣ A, cash the ♡ Q, and lead a *low* spade to partner's known ♠ K. (Declarer has already turned up with 13 high card points and has passed a limit raise). By leading low, you do not set up a spade trick for declarer. If you play ace and a spade you only get one spade trick. This way you get two.

Partner grabs his ♠ K and returns a spade which declarer must either ruff with his last trump or discard a club. In either case the defense comes to five tricks, two spades, two clubs, and the heart queen.

KEY LESSON POINTERS

1. AVOID RUFFING THE LAST WINNER OF A SIDE SUIT WITH THE MASTER TRUMP, PARTICULARLY IF YOU HAVE A CERTAIN SIDE ENTRY. UPON GAINING THE LEAD, YOU CAN CASH YOUR MASTER TRUMP, DRAWING TWO TRUMPS FOR ONE.
2. WHEN DISCARDING A LOSER UPON A WINNER, DECLARER USUALLY DISCARDS FROM THE SHORTER OF TWO REMAINING SIDE SUITS.
3. WHEN DUMMY, NORTH, HAS QJx AND DECLARER A SINGLETON IT IS IMPORTANT THAT EAST, NOT WEST, WIN THE FIRST TRICK IN THE SUIT, OTHERWISE A RUFFING FINESSE MAY BE AVAILABLE.

(98) RULES

East-West vulnerable
Dealer South

North
♠ 8 4 2
♡ K 3
◇ J 4 3
♣ A J 8 6 4

East (you)
♠ K Q 9
♡ 9 8 7 2
◇ K Q 9 8 7
♣ 5

South	West	North	East
1 NT	Pass	3 NT	All Pass

Opening lead: ♠ 6

    You play the ♠ Q and declarer wins the trick. At trick two
declarer leads the ♣ 2, partner plays the ♣ 3 and dummy the
♣ A. At trick three a low club is led from dummy. What do you
discard?

RULES   (Solution)

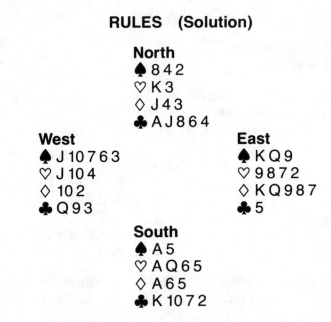

North
- ♠ 8 4 2
- ♡ K 3
- ◇ J 4 3
- ♣ A J 8 6 4

West
- ♠ J 10 7 6 3
- ♡ J 10 4
- ◇ 10 2
- ♣ Q 9 3

East
- ♠ K Q 9
- ♡ 9 8 7 2
- ◇ K Q 9 8 7
- ♣ 5

South
- ♠ A 5
- ♡ A Q 6 5
- ◇ A 6 5
- ♣ K 10 7 2

The ♠ K! The rule of 11 tells you that declarer has only one spade higher than the six. He has used that spade when he won the first trick. In other words, your side is now ready to run the spade suit—but does partner know it?

In order to make life easy for the poor guy sitting across from you, why not let him in on the secret? Discard the ♠ K and let nature take its course.

If you discard something else, partner may get it in his head to shift suits upon winning a possible club trick. Why give him a chance to have an accident?

KEY LESSON POINTERS

1. WHEN LEADING FOURTH BEST, THIRD HAND CAN USE THE RULE OF 11, OFTEN WITH USEFUL RESULTS.
2. WHEN GIVEN A CHANCE TO MAKE A DISCARD, MAKE THE ONE THAT WILL MAKE LIFE EASIEST FOR PARTNER.
3. A GOOD PARTNER BUILDS FENCES AROUND HIS PARTNER—TRYING TO HELP HIM AVOID ERRORS (HAVE ACCIDENTS).

(99)   QUEEN FROM ACE, KING, QUEEN

East-West vulnerable
Dealer South

<pre>
                    North
                    ♠ Q 10 6 5
                    ♡ 8 4 2
                    ◇ A J
                    ♣ K Q J 8
    West (you)
    ♠ K J
    ♡ A K Q 7 3
    ◇ 8 4
    ♣ 10 6 5 2
</pre>

South	West	North	East
Pass	1 ♡	Dbl.	1 NT
2 ♠	All Pass		

Opening lead: ♡ Q

Your opening lead demands count. Partner plays the ♡ J and you continue with the king and ace. Partner follows to the second heart but discards the ♣ 3 on the third heart.

1. What do you play now? Why?

You shift to a high diamond and dummy's jack is covered by the queen and declarer's king. Declarer leads a low spade which you win with the king, partner playing the ♠ 3.

2. What do you play now?

QUEEN FROM ACE, KING, QUEEN   (Solution)

North
♠ Q 10 6 5
♡ 8 4 2
◇ A J
♣ K Q J 8

West
♠ K J
♡ A K Q 7 3
◇ 8 4
♣ 10 6 5 2

East
♠ A 9 3
♡ J 9
◇ Q 10 7 6
♣ 9 7 6 3

South
♠ 8 7 4 2
♡ 10 6 5
◇ K 9 5 3 2
♣ A

1. With partner's discard of a low club, a diamond shift looks reasonable.
2. A heart. Once declarer turns up with the ◇K, the only hope to set the contract lies in the trump suit. If partner's remaining trumps are specifically the A 9, a fourth heart will promote an additional trump trick. Play a heart.

KEY LESSON POINTERS

1. GIVING DECLARER A RUFF AND A SLUFF IS NOT A LOSING PLAY IF DECLARER HAS NO SIDE SUIT LOSERS. IT MAY PROMOTE A TRUMP TRICK FOR PARTNER.
2. THINK POSITIVELY ON DEFENSE AND LOOK FOR SOME REASONABLE HOLDING IN PARTNER'S HAND (CONSISTENT WITH THE BIDDING) THAT WILL GIVE YOU A CHANCE TO DEFEAT THE CONTRACT.

(100) QUANTUM LEAP

East-West vulnerable
Dealer South

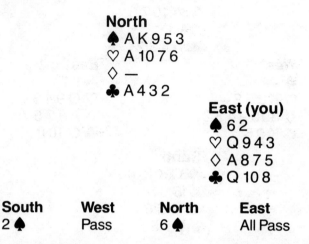

North
♠ A K 9 5 3
♡ A 10 7 6
♢ —
♣ A 4 3 2

East (you)
♠ 6 2
♡ Q 9 4 3
♢ A 8 7 5
♣ Q 10 8

South	West	North	East
2 ♠	Pass	6 ♠	All Pass

Opening lead: ♢ J (Denies a higher honor)

Dummy discards a club. Do you win this trick? If so, what do you return? If not, why not?

QUANTUM LEAP (Solution)

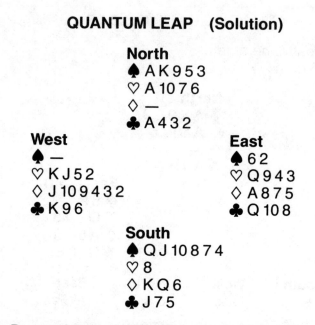

North
♠ A K 9 5 3
♡ A 10 7 6
♢ —
♣ A 4 3 2

West
♠ —
♡ K J 5 2
♢ J 10 9 4 3 2
♣ K 9 6

East
♠ 6 2
♡ Q 9 4 3
♢ A 8 7 5
♣ Q 10 8

South
♠ Q J 10 8 7 4
♡ 8
♢ K Q 6
♣ J 7 5

Do not play the ♢ A! Declarer is marked with the ♢ K Q and if you win your ace declarer will be able to discard two more clubs on the diamonds, leaving dummy with the blank ♣ A.

The fact that declarer did not ruff the opening lead indicates that he has at least three clubs in his hand. As long as declarer can only discard one club from dummy you will still come to two club tricks. If you win the ace, you get the diamond trick but you lose two club tricks. Not a very good deal.

KEY LESSON POINTERS

1. WITH A VOID IN DUMMY, IT MIGHT BE RIGHT TO DUCK AN ACE IF THE SUIT IS LED AND DECLARER IS MARKED WITH BOTH THE KING AND QUEEN. YOU MAY LOSE YOUR ACE, BUT IN TURN YOU PREVENT TWO DISCARDS FROM DUMMY.
2. THIS SAME PRINCIPLE APPLIES WHEN A SINGLETON IS LED FROM DUMMY AND YOU HAVE THE ACE. IF DECLARER HAS BOTH THE KING AND QUEEN, IT COULD BE RIGHT TO DUCK THE TRICK. COURAGE.

APPENDIX (Themes)

1. Reading The Spots—Postponing A Ruff—Visualizing An Overruff
2. Killing Discards—Suit Preference Return Signal
3. Card Combinations—Counting Defensive Tricks
4. Counting Declarer's Hand—Counting Declarer's Points
5. Declining An Overruff
6. Reading Partner's Leads
7. Knowing Which Suit To Discard
8. Getting A Ruff
9. Counting The Hand—Counting Declarer's Points
10. Card Combinations
11. Counting Declarer's Tricks—Card Combinations
12. Promoting Extra Trump Tricks
13. Card Combinations
14. Reading Partner's Attitude Signals
15. Counting Declarer's Tricks—Card Combinations
16. Counting Declarer's Tricks—Killing A Discard
17. Counting The Hand—Counting Defensive Tricks—Inferences
18. Visualizing An Overruff—Cashing A Side Winner First
19. Counting Declarer's Tricks. Visualizing A Winning Defense
20. Trusting Partner—Not Playing Carelessly
21. Counting Declarer's Tricks—Second Hand High—Avoiding A Block
22. Counting The Hand—Card Combinations—Inferences
23. Refusing A Trump Trick—Killing Dummy's Length
24. Killing Discards—Counting Declarer's Hand
25. Counting Declarer's Tricks—Working Out What Declarer Is Trying To Do
26. Defending A 4-3 Trump Fit Holding Axx In The Trump Suit. Ducking Twice
27. Trump Promotion
28. Reading Partner's Cards
29. Giving Yourself Two Chances—Reading Partner's Attitude Signals
30. Reading Partner's Suit Preference Signals
31. Visualizing An Impending End Play—Managing The Ace Of Trumps
32. Counting The Hand—Reading Partner's Count Signal—Counting Tricks

MELVIN POWERS SELF-IMPROVEMENT LIBRARY

_____ SOVIET CHESS *Edited by R. G. Wade*   3.00

COOKERY & HERBS

_____ CULPEPER'S HERBAL REMEDIES *Dr. Nicholas Culpeper*   3.00
_____ FAST GOURMET COOKBOOK *Poppy Cannon*   2.50
_____ GINSENG The Myth & The Truth *Joseph P. Hou*   3.00
_____ HEALING POWER OF HERBS *May Bethel*   4.00
_____ HEALING POWER OF NATURAL FOODS *May Bethel*   5.00
_____ HERB HANDBOOK *Dawn MacLeod*   3.00
_____ HERBS FOR HEALTH—How to Grow & Use Them *Louise Evans Doole*   4.00
_____ HOME GARDEN COOKBOOK—Delicious Natural Food Recipes *Ken Kraft*   3.00
_____ MEDICAL HERBALIST *edited by Dr. J. R. Yemm*   3.00
_____ VEGETABLE GARDENING FOR BEGINNERS *Hugh Wiberg*   2.00
_____ VEGETABLES FOR TODAY'S GARDENS *R. Milton Carleton*   2.00
_____ VEGETARIAN COOKERY *Janet Walker*   4.00
_____ VEGETARIAN COOKING MADE EASY & DELECTABLE *Veronica Vezza*   3.00
_____ VEGETARIAN DELIGHTS—A Happy Cookbook for Health *K. R. Mehta*   2.00
_____ VEGETARIAN GOURMET COOKBOOK *Joyce McKinnel*   3.00

GAMBLING & POKER

_____ ADVANCED POKER STRATEGY & WINNING PLAY *A. D. Livingston*   5.00
_____ HOW TO WIN AT DICE GAMES *Skip Frey*   3.00
_____ HOW TO WIN AT POKER *Terence Reese & Anthony T. Watkins*   5.00
_____ WINNING AT CRAPS *Dr. Lloyd T. Commins*   4.00
_____ WINNING AT GIN *Chester Wander & Cy Rice*   3.00
_____ WINNING AT POKER—An Expert's Guide *John Archer*   5.00
_____ WINNING AT 21—An Expert's Guide *John Archer*   5.00
_____ WINNING POKER SYSTEMS *Norman Zadeh*   3.00

HEALTH

_____ BEE POLLEN *Lynda Lyngheim & Jack Scagnetti*   3.00
_____ DR. LINDNER'S SPECIAL WEIGHT CONTROL METHOD *P. G. Lindner, M.D.*   2.00
_____ HELP YOURSELF TO BETTER SIGHT *Margaret Darst Corbett*   3.00
_____ HOW TO IMPROVE YOUR VISION *Dr. Robert A. Kraskin*   3.00
_____ HOW YOU CAN STOP SMOKING PERMANENTLY *Ernest Caldwell*   3.00
_____ MIND OVER PLATTER *Peter G. Lindner, M.D.*   3.00
_____ NATURE'S WAY TO NUTRITION & VIBRANT HEALTH *Robert J. Scrutton*   3.00
_____ NEW CARBOHYDRATE DIET COUNTER *Patti Lopez-Pereira*   2.00
_____ QUICK & EASY EXERCISES FOR FACIAL BEAUTY *Judy Smith-deal*   2.00
_____ QUICK & EASY EXERCISES FOR FIGURE BEAUTY *Judy Smith-deal*   2.00
_____ REFLEXOLOGY *Dr. Maybelle Segal*   4.00
_____ REFLEXOLOGY FOR GOOD HEALTH *Anna Kaye & Don C. Matchan*   5.00
_____ 30 DAYS TO BEAUTIFUL LEGS *Dr. Marc Selner*   3.00
_____ YOU CAN LEARN TO RELAX *Dr. Samuel Gutwirth*   3.00
_____ YOUR ALLERGY—What To Do About It *Allan Knight, M.D.*   3.00

HOBBIES

_____ BEACHCOMBING FOR BEGINNERS *Norman Hickin*   2.00
_____ BLACKSTONE'S MODERN CARD TRICKS *Harry Blackstone*   3.00
_____ BLACKSTONE'S SECRETS OF MAGIC *Harry Blackstone*   3.00
_____ COIN COLLECTING FOR BEGINNERS *Burton Hobson & Fred Reinfeld*   3.00
_____ ENTERTAINING WITH ESP *Tony 'Doc' Shiels*   2.00
_____ 400 FASCINATING MAGIC TRICKS YOU CAN DO *Howard Thurston*   4.00
_____ HOW I TURN JUNK INTO FUN AND PROFIT *Sari*   3.00
_____ HOW TO WRITE A HIT SONG & SELL IT *Tommy Boyce*   7.00
_____ JUGGLING MADE EASY *Rudolf Dittrich*   3.00
_____ MAGIC FOR ALL AGES *Walter Gibson*   4.00
_____ MAGIC MADE EASY *Byron Wels*   2.00
_____ STAMP COLLECTING FOR BEGINNERS *Burton Hobson*   3.00

HORSE PLAYERS' WINNING GUIDES

_____ BETTING HORSES TO WIN *Les Conklin*   5.00
_____ ELIMINATE THE LOSERS *Bob McKnight*   3.00
_____ HOW TO PICK WINNING HORSES *Bob McKnight*   5.00
_____ HOW TO WIN AT THE RACES *Sam (The Genius) Lewin*   5.00
_____ HOW YOU CAN BEAT THE RACES *Jack Kavanagh*   5.00

____ SEXUALLY ADEQUATE MALE *Frank S. Caprio, M.D.*	3.00
____ SEXUALLY FULFILLED MAN *Dr. Rachel Copelan*	5.00
____ STAYING IN LOVE *Dr. Norton F. Kristy*	7.00

MELVIN POWERS' MAIL ORDER LIBRARY

____ HOW TO GET RICH IN MAIL ORDER *Melvin Powers*	15.00
____ HOW TO WRITE A GOOD ADVERTISEMENT *Victor O. Schwab*	15.00
____ MAIL ORDER MADE EASY *J. Frank Brumbaugh*	10.00
____ U.S. MAIL ORDER SHOPPER'S GUIDE *Susan Spitzer*	10.00

METAPHYSICS & OCCULT

____ BOOK OF TALISMANS, AMULETS & ZODIACAL GEMS *William Pavitt*	7.00
____ CONCENTRATION—A Guide to Mental Mastery *Mouni Sadhu*	5.00
____ CRITIQUES OF GOD *Edited by Peter Angeles*	7.00
____ EXTRA-TERRESTRIAL INTELLIGENCE—The First Encounter	6.00
____ FORTUNE TELLING WITH CARDS *P. Foli*	5.00
____ HANDWRITING ANALYSIS MADE EASY *John Marley*	5.00
____ HANDWRITING TELLS *Nadya Olyanova*	7.00
____ HOW TO INTERPRET DREAMS, OMENS & FORTUNE TELLING SIGNS *Gettings*	5.00
____ HOW TO UNDERSTAND YOUR DREAMS *Geoffrey A. Dudley*	3.00
____ ILLUSTRATED YOGA *William Zorn*	3.00
____ IN DAYS OF GREAT PEACE *Mouni Sadhu*	3.00
____ LSD—THE AGE OF MIND *Bernard Roseman*	2.00
____ MAGICIAN—His Training and Work *W. E. Butler*	3.00
____ MEDITATION *Mouni Sadhu*	7.00
____ MODERN NUMEROLOGY *Morris C. Goodman*	5.00
____ NUMEROLOGY—ITS FACTS AND SECRETS *Ariel Yvon Taylor*	3.00
____ NUMEROLOGY MADE EASY *W. Mykian*	5.00
____ PALMISTRY MADE EASY *Fred Gettings*	5.00
____ PALMISTRY MADE PRACTICAL *Elizabeth Daniels Squire*	5.00
____ PALMISTRY SECRETS REVEALED *Henry Frith*	4.00
____ PROPHECY IN OUR TIME *Martin Ebon*	2.50
____ PSYCHOLOGY OF HANDWRITING *Nadya Olyanova*	7.00
____ SUPERSTITION—Are You Superstitious? *Eric Maple*	2.00
____ TAROT *Mouni Sadhu*	8.00
____ TAROT OF THE BOHEMIANS *Papus*	7.00
____ WAYS TO SELF-REALIZATION *Mouni Sadhu*	3.00
____ WHAT YOUR HANDWRITING REVEALS *Albert E. Hughes*	3.00
____ WITCHCRAFT, MAGIC & OCCULTISM—A Fascinating History *W. B. Crow*	5.00
____ WITCHCRAFT—THE SIXTH SENSE *Justine Glass*	7.00
____ WORLD OF PSYCHIC RESEARCH *Hereward Carrington*	2.00

SELF-HELP & INSPIRATIONAL

____ DAILY POWER FOR JOYFUL LIVING *Dr. Donald Curtis*	5.00
____ DYNAMIC THINKING *Melvin Powers*	3.00
____ GREATEST POWER IN THE UNIVERSE *U. S. Andersen*	5.00
____ GROW RICH WHILE YOU SLEEP *Ben Sweetland*	3.00
____ GROWTH THROUGH REASON *Albert Ellis, Ph.D.*	7.00
____ GUIDE TO PERSONAL HAPPINESS *Albert Ellis, Ph.D. & Irving Becker, Ed. D.*	5.00
____ HELPING YOURSELF WITH APPLIED PSYCHOLOGY *R. Henderson*	2.00
____ HOW TO ATTRACT GOOD LUCK *A. H. Z. Carr*	5.00
____ HOW TO BE GREAT *Dr. Donald Curtis*	5.00
____ HOW TO DEVELOP A WINNING PERSONALITY *Martin Panzer*	5.00
____ HOW TO DEVELOP AN EXCEPTIONAL MEMORY *Young & Gibson*	5.00
____ HOW TO LIVE WITH A NEUROTIC *Albert Ellis, Ph. D.*	5.00
____ HOW TO OVERCOME YOUR FEARS *M. P. Leahy, M.D.*	3.00
____ HOW TO SUCCEED *Brian Adams*	7.00
____ HOW YOU CAN HAVE CONFIDENCE AND POWER *Les Giblin*	5.00
____ HUMAN PROBLEMS & HOW TO SOLVE THEM *Dr. Donald Curtis*	5.00
____ I CAN *Ben Sweetland*	7.00
____ I WILL *Ben Sweetland*	3.00
____ LEFT-HANDED PEOPLE *Michael Barsley*	5.00
____ MAGIC IN YOUR MIND *U. S. Andersen*	7.00
____ MAGIC OF THINKING BIG *Dr. David J. Schwartz*	3.00

____	MAGIC POWER OF YOUR MIND *Walter M. Germain*	7.00
____	MENTAL POWER THROUGH SLEEP SUGGESTION *Melvin Powers*	3.00
____	NEW GUIDE TO RATIONAL LIVING *Albert Ellis, Ph.D. & R. Harper, Ph.D.*	3.00
____	PROJECT YOU *A Manual of Rational Assertiveness Training Paris & Casey*	6.00
____	PSYCHO-CYBERNETICS *Maxwell Maltz, M.D.*	5.00
____	SALES CYBERNETICS *Brian Adams*	7.00
____	SCIENCE OF MIND IN DAILY LIVING *Dr. Donald Curtis*	5.00
____	SECRET OF SECRETS *U. S. Andersen*	7.00
____	SECRET POWER OF THE PYRAMIDS *U. S. Andersen*	7.00
____	SELF-THERAPY FOR THE STUTTERER *Malcolm Fraser*	3.00
____	STUTTERING AND WHAT YOU CAN DO ABOUT IT *W. Johnson, Ph.D.*	2.50
____	SUCCESS-CYBERNETICS *U. S. Andersen*	6.00
____	10 DAYS TO A GREAT NEW LIFE *William E. Edwards*	3.00
____	THINK AND GROW RICH *Napoleon Hill*	5.00
____	THINK YOUR WAY TO SUCCESS *Dr. Lew Losoncy*	5.00
____	THREE MAGIC WORDS *U. S. Andersen*	7.00
____	TREASURY OF COMFORT *edited by Rabbi Sidney Greenberg*	5.00
____	TREASURY OF THE ART OF LIVING *Sidney S. Greenberg*	5.00
____	YOU ARE NOT THE TARGET *Laura Huxley*	5.00
____	YOUR SUBCONSCIOUS POWER *Charles M. Simmons*	5.00
____	YOUR THOUGHTS CAN CHANGE YOUR LIFE *Dr. Donald Curtis*	5.00

SPORTS

____	BICYCLING FOR FUN AND GOOD HEALTH *Kenneth E. Luther*	2.00
____	BILLIARDS—Pocket • Carom • Three Cushion *Clive Cottingham, Jr.*	5.00
____	CAMPING-OUT 101 Ideas & Activities *Bruno Knobel*	2.00
____	COMPLETE GUIDE TO FISHING *Vlad Evanoff*	2.00
____	HOW TO IMPROVE YOUR RACQUETBALL *Lubarsky Kaufman & Scagnetti*	3.00
____	HOW TO WIN AT POCKET BILLIARDS *Edward D. Knuchell*	5.00
____	JOY OF WALKING *Jack Scagnetti*	3.00
____	LEARNING & TEACHING SOCCER SKILLS *Eric Worthington*	3.00
____	MOTORCYCLING FOR BEGINNERS *I. G. Edmonds*	3.00
____	RACQUETBALL FOR WOMEN *Toni Hudson, Jack Scagnetti & Vince Rondone*	3.00
____	RACQUETBALL MADE EASY *Steve Lubarsky, Rod Delson & Jack Scagnetti*	4.00
____	SECRET OF BOWLING STRIKES *Dawson Taylor*	5.00
____	SECRET OF PERFECT PUTTING *Horton Smith & Dawson Taylor*	5.00
____	SOCCER—The Game & How to Play It *Gary Rosenthal*	5.00
____	STARTING SOCCER *Edward F. Dolan, Jr.*	3.00

TENNIS LOVERS' LIBRARY

____	BEGINNER'S GUIDE TO WINNING TENNIS *Helen Hull Jacobs*	2.00
____	HOW TO BEAT BETTER TENNIS PLAYERS *Loring Fiske*	4.00
____	HOW TO IMPROVE YOUR TENNIS—Style, Strategy & Analysis *C. Wilson*	2.00
____	PLAY TENNIS WITH ROSEWALL *Ken Rosewall*	2.00
____	PSYCH YOURSELF TO BETTER TENNIS *Dr. Walter A. Luszki*	2.00
____	TENNIS FOR BEGINNERS, *Dr. H. A. Murray*	2.00
____	TENNIS MADE EASY *Joel Brecheen*	4.00
____	WEEKEND TENNIS—How to Have Fun & Win at the Same Time *Bill Talbert*	3.00
____	WINNING WITH PERCENTAGE TENNIS—Smart Strategy *Jack Lowe*	2.00

WILSHIRE PET LIBRARY

____	DOG OBEDIENCE TRAINING *Gust Kessopulos*	5.00
____	DOG TRAINING MADE EASY & FUN *John W. Kellogg*	4.00
____	HOW TO BRING UP YOUR PET DOG *Kurt Unkelbach*	2.00
____	HOW TO RAISE & TRAIN YOUR PUPPY *Jeff Griffen*	5.00
____	PIGEONS: HOW TO RAISE & TRAIN THEM *William H. Allen, Jr.*	2.00

The books listed above can be obtained from your book dealer or directly from Melvin Powers. When ordering, please remit $1.00 postage for the first book and 50¢ for each additional book.

Melvin Powers

12015 Sherman Road, No. Hollywood, California 91605

WILSHIRE HORSE LOVERS' LIBRARY

_____ AMATEUR HORSE BREEDER *A. C. Leighton Hardman*	5.00
_____ AMERICAN QUARTER HORSE IN PICTURES *Margaret Cabell Self*	3.00
_____ APPALOOSA HORSE *Donna & Bill Richardson*	7.00
_____ ARABIAN HORSE *Reginald S. Summerhays*	5.00
_____ ART OF WESTERN RIDING *Suzanne Norton Jones*	5.00
_____ AT THE HORSE SHOW *Margaret Cabell Self*	3.00
_____ BACK-YARD HORSE *Peggy Jett Pittinger*	4.00
_____ BASIC DRESSAGE *Jean Froissard*	5.00
_____ BEGINNER'S GUIDE TO HORSEBACK RIDING *Sheila Wall*	2.00
_____ BEGINNER'S GUIDE TO THE WESTERN HORSE *Natlee Kenoyer*	2.00
_____ BITS—THEIR HISTORY, USE AND MISUSE *Louis Taylor*	5.00
_____ BREAKING & TRAINING THE DRIVING HORSE *Doris Ganton*	10.00
_____ BREAKING YOUR HORSE'S BAD HABITS *W. Dayton Sumner*	5.00
_____ COMPLETE TRAINING OF HORSE AND RIDER *Colonel Alois Podhajsky*	6.00
_____ DISORDERS OF THE HORSE & WHAT TO DO ABOUT THEM *E. Hanauer*	5.00
_____ DOG TRAINING MADE EASY & FUN *John W. Kellogg*	4.00
_____ DRESSAGE—A Study of the Finer Points in Riding *Henry Wynmalen*	7.00
_____ DRIVE ON *Doris Ganton*	7.00
_____ DRIVING HORSES *Sallie Walrond*	5.00
_____ EQUITATION *Jean Froissard*	5.00
_____ FIRST AID FOR HORSES *Dr. Charles H. Denning, Jr.*	3.00
_____ FUN OF RAISING A COLT *Rubye & Frank Griffith*	5.00
_____ FUN ON HORSEBACK *Margaret Caball Self*	4.00
_____ GYMKHANA GAMES *Natlee Kenoyer*	2.00
_____ HORSE DISEASES—Causes, Symptoms & Treatment *Dr. H. G. Belschner*	6.00
_____ HORSE OWNER'S CONCISE GUIDE *Elsie V. Hanauer*	3.00
_____ HORSE SELECTION & CARE FOR BEGINNERS *George H. Conn*	7.00
_____ HORSEBACK RIDING FOR BEGINNERS *Louis Taylor*	7.00
_____ HORSEBACK RIDING MADE EASY & FUN *Sue Henderson Coen*	7.00
_____ HORSES—Their Selection, Care & Handling *Margaret Cabell Self*	5.00
_____ HOW TO BUY A BETTER HORSE & SELL THE HORSE YOU OWN	3.00
_____ HOW TO ENJOY YOUR QUARTER HORSE *Willard H. Porter*	3.00
_____ HUNTER IN PICTURES *Margaret Cabell Self*	2.00
_____ ILLUSTRATED BOOK OF THE HORSE *S. Sidney* (8½" × 11")	10.00
_____ ILLUSTRATED HORSE MANAGEMENT—400 Illustrations *Dr. E. Mayhew*	6.00
_____ ILLUSTRATED HORSE TRAINING *Captain M. H. Hayes*	7.00
_____ ILLUSTRATED HORSEBACK RIDING FOR BEGINNERS *Jeanne Mellin*	3.00
_____ JUMPING—Learning & Teaching *Jean Froissard*	5.00
_____ KNOW ALL ABOUT HORSES *Harry Disston*	3.00
_____ LAME HORSE Cause, Symptoms & Treatment *Dr. James R. Rooney*	7.00
_____ LAW & YOUR HORSE *Edward H. Greene*	7.00
_____ MANUAL OF HORSEMANSHIP *Harold Black*	5.00
_____ MOVIE HORSES—The Fascinating Techniques of Training *Anthony Amaral*	2.00
_____ POLICE HORSES *Judith Campbell*	2.00
_____ PRACTICAL GUIDE TO HORSESHOEING	5.00
_____ PRACTICAL GUIDE TO OWNING YOUR OWN HORSE *Steven D. Price*	3.00
_____ PRACTICAL HORSE PSYCHOLOGY *Moyra Williams*	5.00
_____ PROBLEM HORSES Guide for Curing Serious Behavior Habits *Summerhays*	4.00
_____ REINSMAN OF THE WEST—BRIDLES & BITS *Ed Connell*	5.00
_____ RIDE WESTERN *Louis Taylor*	5.00
_____ SCHOOLING YOUR YOUNG HORSE *George Wheatley*	5.00
_____ STABLE MANAGEMENT FOR THE OWNER-GROOM *George Wheatley*	4.00
_____ STALLION MANAGEMENT—A Guide for Stud Owners *A. C. Hardman*	5.00
_____ TEACHING YOUR HORSE TO JUMP *W. J. Froud*	5.00
_____ TRAINING YOUR HORSE TO SHOW *Neale Haley*	5.00
_____ TREATING COMMON DISEASES OF YOUR HORSE *Dr. George H. Conn*	5.00
_____ TREATING HORSE AILMENTS *G. W. Serth*	2.00
_____ YOU AND YOUR PONY *Pepper Mainwaring Healey* (8½" × 11")	6.00
_____ YOUR FIRST HORSE *George C. Saunders, M.D.*	5.00
_____ YOUR PONY BOOK *Hermann Wiederhold*	2.00

The books listed above can be obtained from your book dealer or directly from Melvin Powers. When ordering, please remit $1.00 postage for the first book and 50¢ for each additional book.

Melvin Powers

12015 Sherman Road, No. Hollywood, California 91605

NOTES

NOTES

NOTES

NOTES

NOTES